SENSE AND SENSIBILITY

BY KATE HAMILL

BASED ON THE NOVEL BY
JANE AUSTEN

DRAMATISTS
PLAY SERVICE
INC.

NOTE ON BILLING

Anyone receiving permission to produce SENSE AND SENSIBILITY is required to give credit to the Author as sole and exclusive Author of the Play on the title page of all programs distributed in connection with performances of the Play and in all instances in which the title of the Play appears, including printed or digital materials for advertising, publicizing or otherwise exploiting the Play and/or a production thereof. Please see your production license for font size and typeface requirements.

Be advised that there may be additional credits required in all programs and promotional material. Such language will be listed under the "Additional Billing" section of production licenses. It is the licensee's responsibility to ensure any and all required billing is included in the requisite places, per the terms of the license.

SPECIAL NOTE ON SONGS/RECORDINGS

Dramatists Play Service neither holds the rights to nor grants permission to use any songs or recordings mentioned in the Play. Permission for performances of copyrighted songs, arrangements or recordings mentioned in this Play is not included in our license agreement. The permission of the copyright owner(s) must be obtained for any such use. For any songs and/or recordings mentioned in the Play, other songs, arrangements, or recordings may be substituted provided permission from the copyright owner(s) of such songs, arrangements or recordings is obtained; or songs, arrangements or recordings in the public domain may be substituted.

Dedicated to John Buxton.
We love and miss you, John.

ACKNOWLEDGMENTS

First and foremost, I must thank everyone in the Bedlam family—especially Eric Tucker and Andrus Nichols. Thanks also to the wonderful Beth Blickers, Jason O'Connell, Jane Guyer-Fujita, Sarah Rasmussen, Davis McCallum, Janine Nabers, Jose Rivera, and Jamie Lewis (who looked over *S&S* to ensure historical accuracy). Thanks also to my loved ones for their support—especially my family.

The world premiere of SENSE AND SENSIBILITY was produced by Bedlam (Eric Tucker, Artistic Director; Andrus Nichols, Producing Director) at the Sheen Center in New York City, on November 10, 2014. It was directed by Eric Tucker. The set design was by John McDermott; the lighting design was by Les Dickert; the costume design was by Angela Huff; the sound design was by Eric Tucker and Katie Young; the assistant director was Aubrey Snowden; the choreography was by Alexandra Beller; the dramaturg was Emily Lyon; the dialect coach was Amanda Quaid; the production stage manager was Katharine Whitney; the assistant stage manager was Violeta Picayo; and the historical fact-checker was Jamie Lewis. The cast was as follows (in alphabetical order):

FANNY DASHWOOD/LUCY STEELE/
LADY MIDDLETON/GOSSIP .... Laura Baranik
COLONEL BRANDON/THOMAS/
LADY MIDDLETON/GOSSIP .... Nigel Gore
MARIANNE DASHWOOD .... Kate Hamill
ELINOR DASHWOOD .... Andrus Nichols
EDWARD FERRARS/ROBERT FERRARS/
LADY MIDDLETON/GOSSIP .... Jason O'Connell
JOHN WILLOUGHBY/
JOHN DASHWOOD/GOSSIP .... John Russell
MARGARET DASHWOOD/
MRS. FERRARS/GOSSIP .... Vaishnavi Sharma
MRS. DASHWOOD/
ANNE STEELE/GOSSIP .... Samantha Steinmetz
MRS. JENNINGS/GOSSIP .... Eric Tucker
JOHN MIDDLETON/DOCTOR/
SERVANT/GOSSIP .... Stephan Wolfert

CHARACTERS

ELINOR DASHWOOD—the eldest Dashwood sister; sensible.

MARIANNE DASHWOOD—the middle Dashwood sister; sensitive.

MARGARET DASHWOOD—the youngest Dashwood sister; 10–13 years old.

MRS. DASHWOOD—mother to the Dashwood sisters.

JOHN DASHWOOD—half-brother to the Dashwood sisters (from their father's side; no blood relation to Mrs. Dashwood).

EDWARD FERRARS—a gentleman; a bachelor.

FANNY (FERRARS) DASHWOOD—wife to John Dashwood and sister to Edward; nasty.

COLONEL BRANDON—an older bachelor; over 45 years old.

JOHN WILLOUGHBY—an unusually handsome young man.

SIR JOHN MIDDLETON—a country gentleman; distant relation to Mrs. Dashwood.

MRS. JENNINGS—a good-natured, boisterous woman; mother-in-law to Sir John and a terror to the countryside.

LADY MIDDLETON—an over-bred lady.

LUCY STEELE—a young girl from no fortune.

ANNE STEELE—Lucy's sister; indiscreet.

ROBERT FERRARS—a callow young man; Edward Ferrars' younger brother.

Also, to be doubled with the cast:

GOSSIPS 1–5—a chorus of high-society creatures.

SERVANTS—including THOMAS.

DOCTOR

PLACE & TIME

England, 1790s.

NOTE

This play may be performed with as little or as much in the way of set, props, or spectacle as you prefer—in Bedlam's world premiere, it was ingeniously staged with a few pieces of simple furniture. I encourage you to be as creative as you wish; it's meant to be a bit of a funhouse! Doubling is also encouraged; the only characters that absolutely should not be doubled are Elinor and Marianne, as the "sense" and "sensibility" foci of the piece. The Gossips may be assigned as needed. Have fun—Jane Austen would approve.

SENSE AND SENSIBILITY

ACT ONE

The Gossips

The Gossips, a chorus of high-society creatures, enter. They chatter away happily—in late eighteenth-century England, gossip (and a reputation created by that gossip) is lifeblood and social stricture and pastime and national sport and destiny. Whether or not it is delineated in the script, the Gossips are often watching or whispering or contributing to the action. The intent is to create an atmosphere in which someone is almost always observing and judging. It is oppressive and constricting, but not necessarily unfriendly; it is all great fun for the Gossips. The Gossips gather around a table, poised and ready to burst...

GOSSIP 1. Did I tell you, I saw Lady Fagg and all of her five daughters last week...

> *All of the Gossips burst into speech simultaneously, in a great cacophony of sound, like gulls squabbling over food, talking over each other. They do not have to get through all of the dialogue.*

GOSSIP 2.
The Miss Dashwoods are highly thought of throughout all the county, I think! Elinor Dashwood is said to possess a strength of understanding, and coolness of judgment, and yet an affectionate disposition. Marianne Dashwood

GOSSIP 1.
...with old Mrs. Hamilton, from Canterbury, and Miss Chapman, from Margate, into the bargain. I never saw so plain a family—five sisters so very plain! They are as plain as the Foresters, or the Franfraddops,

9

is a lively enough girl, eager in all she does. I should think any young man who made a connection with the Miss Dashwoods should have little reason to regret it!

or the Seagraves, or the Rivers—excluding Miss Sophy, Miss Sally Fagg has some kind of a figure, and that compromises all the good looks of the family. It was stupidish; there was a lack of talk altogether.

GOSSIP 3.
Dead of a fright, they say—I suppose he happened to look at his wife. I do not know what the Faggs should have for mourning. Perhaps bombazeen and crape, according to what is now almost universal. I wonder if it is too recent for the cousins to attend the gala on Tuesday? There is to be a concert, with illuminations and fireworks. Even the concert will have more than its usual charm for me, as the gardens are large enough for me to get pretty well beyond the reach of its sound!

GOSSIP 4.
It would be a fine match on her side, at least. I never thought the Miss Bennets anything *exceptional*, but they would pass as beauties in this county. Now Dorsetshire has *true* beauties; I met Lady Honeywood there, you know. I did not sit near enough to be a perfect judge, but I thought her extremely pretty, and her manners have all the recommendations of ease; and going about with four horses and nicely dressed herself, she is altogether a perfect sort of woman.

GOSSIP 5. Well, we shall see. I find the Bingleys rather plain, but then there are very few true beautiful girls in the world. I respect Miss Chamberlayne for doing her hair well, but I cannot feel a more tender sentiment. Miss Langley is like any other short girl, with a broad nose and wide mouth, fashionable dress and exposed bosom. Mrs. Blount is much admired—with her broad face, diamond bandeau, white shoes, pink husband, and fat neck!

> *With no great ceremony, a body is dropped upon the table, as for a funeral. The Gossips stare at it a moment before speaking, then gather around it.*

The Dashwoods

GOSSIP 1. Poor Mr. Dashwood—carried away so suddenly! Woke one morning with a fever, and drew his last gasp within the week! *(Overlapping with next line.)* Poor Mr. Dashwood!

GOSSIP 2. Poor Mr. Dashwood! But a very handsome funeral. The serenity of the corpse was most delightful. *(Overlapping with next line.)* Poor Mr. Dashwood!

GOSSIP 3. Poor Mr. Dashwood! And poor *Mrs.* Dashwood, in every sense of the word! You know that his widow and daughters are left with almost nothing!

> *The Gossips, drawn sharply to this information, drop all interest in the corpse.*

GOSSIP 4. No!

GOSSIP 1. Not truly?

GOSSIP 4. But Norland Park is such a large estate!

GOSSIP 2. Were there... *(In hushed tones.)* very many DEBTS in the family?

GOSSIP 3. No, nothing like that. *(Officiously.)* It was a question of the law!

GOSSIP 4. DID SOMEBODY BREAK THE LAW?

> *The Gossips all shush him.*

GOSSIP 3. No, no. Mr. Dashwood could not *legally* bequeath it to the ladies.

> *The Gossips are a bit disappointed.*

It all went to his son from the previous marriage, Mr. John Dashwood.

> *John Dashwood enters.*

JOHN. I think that I will give them a thousand pounds apiece to start their new life!

GOSSIP 4. But wasn't he a rich man already?

GOSSIP 3. Oh yes, he married into money. But his rich wife— *(Lowers voice.)* not a sympathetic creature! Moved into Norland Park the DAY AFTER THE FUNERAL, without a word of notice to the new widow!

Fanny Dashwood enters; all the Gossips "tsk" reprovingly.

FANNY. My dear John, how can you think of taking four thousand pounds from the fortune of our dear little boy? What possible claim can the Miss Dashwoods, who are only related to you by half blood, have to so large an amount?

JOHN. My father's last request was that I provide for them, Fanny.

FANNY. Your father did not know what he was talking of, I dare say; ten to one he was light-headed at the time. Four thousand pounds!

JOHN. He did not specify any particular amount.

Fanny waits.

Perhaps if the sum were diminished by one-half. Five hundred pounds apiece would be a great increase to their fortunes!

FANNY. Two thousand pounds! What brother on earth would do so much for even his REAL sisters!

JOHN. One had rather do too much than too little. Do you think that they may expect more?

FANNY. Who knows what they may expect.

JOHN. Two thousand pounds, all at once, might overwhelm them and be spent unwisely, I suppose. Perhaps a yearly sum, instead?

FANNY. People always live forever when there is an annuity to be paid them. To be very honest, my love, I am convinced that your father had no idea of you giving them any *money*. I wager when he told you to "provide for them," he meant to help them to move their things, and send them occasional presents of fish and game, and so forth. My darling—may I risk being perfectly frank?

JOHN. Always, my angel.

FANNY. The painful truth is that even on his deathbed, your father was not thinking of us, nor of our little Harry—he thought only of THEM. So you owe no particular attention to his wishes, for given his way, he would have left them everything in the world. Remember, my dear—he left them all the best china.

JOHN. The china is a material consideration. It is absolutely unnecessary to do more, I think, than to help them move comfortably. How liberal and handsome you are, my lamb.

She takes his arm. They exit.

GOSSIP 1. And so the young ladies and their mother are left in such reduced circumstances! How shall the girls ever catch a man?

GOSSIP 3. As to that, I understand Mrs. John Dashwood's brother, Mr. Edward Ferrars, is to stay with his sister at Norland for a time. He is a bachelor...

GOSSIP 4. —and stands to inherit a large fortune from his mother!

GOSSIP 3. If one of the Dashwoods could make a catch of *him*...

Edward and Elinor

The Gossips turn with great speculative interest towards Elinor, the eldest Dashwood sister, sitting at a table in the parlor at Norland Park. She is attempting to write a letter. Edward Ferrars enters. Edward is awkward, shy, but fundamentally sweet. He also carries pen and paper, to write a letter.

EDWARD. *(Looks up and sees Elinor.)* Oh! Please do excuse me.

He turns to flee.

ELINOR. Mr. Ferrars.

EDWARD. Miss Dashwood. Please pardon me. I did not...I do not intend to intrude.

He turns to leave, giving a hurried half-bow, and drops the pen and paper—leading to an undignified scramble. He is mortified. It is very endearing. This may be the first time that either Elinor or Edward has been completely alone with an eligible member of the opposite sex—ever.

ELINOR. Oh, no. You weren't. Intruding. Are you, ah— *(Indicating his paper.)*

EDWARD. —Yes. I am. Writing. A letter, yes. Oh. Are you, I see— are you as well?

ELINOR. I am. Writing, yes.

He almost turns to leave again.

Mr. Ferrars. Pray, do not leave? On my account. That is...the light—is very good here.

13

She indicates a seat at the other end of the table. Edward half-bows again, his hands full of paper and pen. He awkwardly staggers over and spills his now-scattered materials across the table; Elinor steadies her ink. They sit in silence for a moment, unsure of what to do. Edward searches for his ink, but realizes he has forgotten it—the only ink is by Elinor. She holds it up in invitation. In order to reach the ink, he either has to lean across the whole length of the table or walk over to her. Choosing to be brave, he stands up, walks over to the ink, and dips in his quill; he's quite close to her. Everything about the moment is awkward. He walks back to his seat, holding his hand beneath the quill, which is now dripping ink everywhere. He sits and puts his pen to paper, but does not write. There is another brief moment of silence.

EDWARD. Miss Dashwood. I fear I have not yet had a proper occasion to express to you, ah, personally, my very sincere condolences on the loss of your father.

ELINOR. Oh. Yes. Thank you.

Another pause. They bend their heads to writing; neither of them is able to write. He clears his throat.

EDWARD. Miss Dashwood. I hope that my presence here has not caused you any...additional distress in this sad time. My sister—I confess, I was not entirely informed of all the particular...particulars before my visit.

ELINOR. Oh. No. You needn't apologize, Mr. Ferrars. In fact, I must thank you—My mother said only yesterday that your presence at Norland is a comfort, and I am very grateful for anything that raises her spirits.

EDWARD. I am pleased that your mother is...pleased. *(Mentally kicking himself for that.)* That is, ah. Might I enquire after Mrs. Dashwood?

ELINOR. It is rather too early to think of any moderation in grief. My father's death—it is very difficult.

She attempts not to get emotional.

EDWARD. I am sure that you must be a great comfort to her.

ELINOR. I attempt to be.

Small pause.

I am writing to our cousin, Sir John Middleton. He may have a cottage available for us in Devonshire. The rent is uncommonly moderate.

EDWARD. I imagine it must be very difficult. To leave your home.

ELINOR. Yes. We were...we have been very happy here.

She attempts not to cry.

I must not smudge this.

EDWARD. Miss Dashwood...please forgive me, I fear—I did not mean to upset you—

Edward impulsively takes out his handkerchief and brings it over to her, half-kneeling. Elinor takes it, slightly mortified.

ELINOR. Mr. Ferrars. I cannot use this.

She shows him. There is ink all over the handkerchief, from his stained hand. There is a moment of awkwardness; then she begins to laugh a little. They both begin to laugh a little, despite themselves.

EDWARD. Miss Dashwood, I beg your pardon...no, this is inexcusable...I am very, very sorry...

ELINOR. Oh, no—it's very—it's very kind of you—I beg YOUR pardon... Oh no, no, please stop, you're going to smear it...

Fanny comes in and absorbs it all, Edward kneeling very close to Elinor. Edward looks up and starts guiltily, which makes it worse.

EDWARD. Fanny! Miss Dashwood was just—she was kind enough to—

FANNY. Edward. There is *ink* on your *face.*

Elinor and Edward freeze like guilty children. Edward turns away from Elinor. Slowly, haltingly, Edward begins to speak as we transition to:

EDWARD.
>Thus conscience does make cowards of us all
>And thus the native hue of resolution
>Is sicklied o'er with the pale cast of thought—

>>*Marianne, the middle Dashwood sister, and Mrs. Dashwood enter as Fanny exits, looking balefully at Edward. Elinor sketches a portrait of Edward; Mrs. Dashwood embroiders. Edward reads from a copy of* Hamlet.

MARIANNE. With spirit, Edward!

EDWARD. *(Getting worse.)*
>And enterprises of great pith and moment—

MARIANNE. *(Can hardly keep her seat.)* Edward, please. Hamlet is not making polite conversation! In this speech, he is all of man-kind—all of humankind—railing against the forces that would keep us tame—that prevent us from acting upon our soul's truest impulses. It is a desperate cry against the futility of a life less than entirely lived! You must be driven almost mad by PASSION, by RAGE, by love for the FRAIL BEAUTY OF LIFE ITSELF!

EDWARD. *(Getting even worse.)*
>With this regard their currents turn away—

MARIANNE. Edward, Shakespeare writes in a rhythm—

>>*Pounds iambically on the table, ba-bum ba-bum ba-bum.*

which matches precisely the beats of the human heart. If your heart also beats—which I presume it does—

EDWARD. …Yes?

MARIANNE. —Then you cannot help but feel the impossible depth of all of Hamlet's text!
>And thus the native hue of resolution
>Is sicklied o'er with the pale cast of thought—

EDWARD. *(As she claps the meter at him.)*
>…With THIS reGARD their CURrents TURN aWAY
>And LOSE the NAME of ACTion—

MARIANNE. *(Unsubtly turning him to face Elinor.)*
Soft you now!
The fair Ophelia!

ELINOR. Marianne.

EDWARD.
Soft YOU now!
The FAIR OpHELia!

MARIANNE. *(Milking it.)*
Nymph, in thy orisons—

EDWARD. *(To Elinor.)*
NYMPH, in THY orISONS,
Be ALL my SINS reMEMber'd!

Pause. Mrs. Dashwood politely claps.

MARIANNE. Oh, Edward.

She takes Hamlet *from him.*

EDWARD. I'm sorry.

MRS. DASHWOOD. A noble effort! *(Aside.)* Why would you give him *Hamlet* to begin, Marianne?

MARIANNE. Nay, Mamma, if one is not to be animated by *Hamlet*! *(With an effort to be polite.)* —But I suppose we must allow for differences of taste.

EDWARD. In truth, you have done me a service. I may now tell my mother in all seriousness that I have no talent for public speaking.

MRS. DASHWOOD. Will she take such a defeat willingly, Edward? Your sister is always telling us you are destined to be a very great orator.

EDWARD. My life's work seems to be to convince both Fanny and my mother that I am unsuited for public scrutiny.

MRS. DASHWOOD. Then how is your fame to be established? For famous you must be to satisfy them!

EDWARD. I cannot be forced into greatness, thank heaven.

MRS. DASHWOOD. And do you have no ambition?

EDWARD. My ambition is to be happy, but I fear it must be in my own way. Wealth and fame would not make me so.

MARIANNE. Strange that it would! What has wealth or fame to do with being happy?

ELINOR. Wealth has much to do with it.

MARIANNE. Elinor, for shame!

ELINOR. Money determines more than you might wish, Marianne.

Margaret enters.

MARGARET. Edward, you promised me you would show me Fancy's new puppies before dinner.

EDWARD. I did. Shall we make a party of it?

MARIANNE. I have seen them already.

Elinor, smiling, shakes her head no.

MRS. DASHWOOD. It must be a quick visit, Margaret. Please do wear your boots—it's raining.

MARGARET. I don't know where they are.

MARIANNE. It's scarcely raining, Mamma—

MRS. DASHWOOD. *(Already up and shooing Margaret out.)* Let us ask Betsy if they've been laid aside.

The three exit. Pause. Elinor continues to sketch.

MARIANNE. What a pity it is, Elinor, that Edward reads so spiritlessly.

ELINOR. Marianne, you have been hectoring him all afternoon, and you have only made him more self-conscious. If you would leave him alone for a moment, I'm sure that he would read very well indeed.

MARIANNE. I was only trying to help.

ELINOR. Mm.

MARIANNE. Elinor, are you truly offended?

ELINOR. Do you really think him spiritless?

MARIANNE. I have the highest opinion possible of Edward, I assure you! I think him every thing in the world that is worthy and amiable.

ELINOR. *(Slightly mollified.)* Must you always speak so warmly?

MARIANNE. Don't you agree?

ELINOR. I think that Edward is very…sensible. His mind is excellent, and if he is not always a brilliant orator, it is only shyness that impedes him.

MARIANNE. Indeed.

ELINOR. He may sometimes appear awkward. But I believe that is only because he strives so earnestly never to hurt any living creature by careless thought or action.

MARIANNE. Yes.

ELINOR. —I grant you, perhaps he is not fashionable.

MARIANNE. No—

ELINOR. —Perhaps he is not even widely considered "handsome." But once you notice his eyes, which are uncommonly good, and consider the general sweetness of his expression…well, I find him very handsome indeed. *(Self-consciously going back to her drawing.)* But what say you, Marianne?

MARIANNE. I swear that when you tell me to love him as a brother, I shall think him perfect indeed.

ELINOR. Marianne! I do not deny that I think very highly of Edward.

> *Marianne springs up.*

That I greatly esteem him! That I like him.

MARIANNE. *Esteem* him! *Like* him! Cold-hearted Elinor!

ELINOR. Excuse me for speaking in so quiet a way of my feelings. Believe them to be stronger than I have declared. But I am not sure that Edward feels anything for me beyond friendship.

MARIANNE. Elinor.

ELINOR. He may have a kind of a…preference!

MARIANNE. Ah-ha!

ELINOR. But there are other points to be considered, Marianne! He is dependent on his mother for a living, and must obey her wishes in all things. Edward would face many obstacles if he wished to marry a woman with no fortune.

> *A servant enters. They hush.*

SERVANT. Miss Dashwood. Dinner is served.

MARIANNE. *(As soon as the servant leaves.)* You must not be diffident, Elinor! Edward is obviously desperately in love with you, and no material obstacle can stand in the way of love for long. That means it is only a matter of time…

ELINOR. Before?

MARIANNE. Before he binds his soul to yours, forever!

ELINOR. …Where do you pick up these phrases?

Marianne pokes her.

Stop! You are a goose.

Marianne pokes her many times, she flees.

Stop, we must go in for dinner!

Rather giggly, they head into dinner.

Dinner

The family, including John and Fanny, sits down to dinner. It is tense. Only Margaret chatters away.

MARGARET. There was a brown one, and a white one, and one that was almost all white, but with a brown spot on his ear. They were all so sweet! Do you think, Mamma, I may be able to have one as my particular pet? She could sleep in the barn.

MRS. DASHWOOD. We shall see, my dear. I do not know how much room we shall have. In the new house.

Awkward pause.

JOHN. How fortunate, ma'am, that you were able to find lodging so soon! We are very sorry to lose you, of course.

FANNY. When, exactly, are you planning to move?

MRS. DASHWOOD. I might have immediate possession of the cottage, but I imagine it will be some months before we put all the particulars to rights.

EDWARD. I do not think it right that you are moving so far away.

MRS. DASHWOOD. Not too far to visit. Fanny, you and John will always be welcome. And Edward—I hope you will also come and stay with us very soon?

EDWARD. I will, certainly. I will certainly visit soon.

FANNY. But not too soon, Edward—we would not want you to cut short your visit here, and then you have so many other obligations. You know that *Maman* expects you next month—when *(Significantly.)* Miss Morton is visiting...

EDWARD. I am not even acquainted with Miss Morton, Fanny. I am sure that I can manage both.

FANNY. Edward. Do not make promises that you cannot keep.

> *Moment of awkward silence. Fanny addresses this to the table at large:*

My brother, you know, is soft-hearted, and always wishes to please everybody at every time. But we must not allow him to become too distracted! We have such great expectations for him. There is truly no limit to what Edward may accomplish—whether in the army, the law, or the government.

JOHN. Hear, hear!

FANNY. You know, it is quite burdensome to have such very very high potential, as our Edward does. And I confess, it does make me fear for him.

JOHN. What do you mean, my love?

FANNY. Why, my poor brother is a fox—and hallooing all around him are hunters and hounds. *(Doing an extremely ladylike imitation of a hound.)* Aooo, aooo.

JOHN. A fox, Fanny?

FANNY. Oh, I am sorry—am I being very abstract? He is a target, my love. He is...prey. Opportunists are always circling, eager to pounce. An eligible man of my brother's station will always attract, for example—upwardly-minded young ladies. There is no predator so fierce, no creature so shameless, as an unmarried woman in the desperate pursuit of a wealthy man. It is a sad reflection of our libertine age, but I assure you that such fortune-hunters are all too common—and I do use that term broadly.

EDWARD. Fanny!

FANNY. What? I am merely making conversation.

MRS. DASHWOOD. *(She can take no more.)* I misspoke earlier. We shall remove ourselves from this house within a week, no matter the expense. I have lost my appetite. Girls, come.

She sweeps out. Marianne, Elinor, and Margaret follow. Fanny, John, and Edward sit at the table for a moment by themselves.

FANNY. Aooo, aooo.

The Gossips sweep on and hurriedly pack up the table and belongings. As they do, Edward walks up to Elinor.

EDWARD. Miss Dashwood. I wanted to say…

He sticks out a hand.

Very safe travels to your new home.

Elinor and Edward awkwardly shake hands goodbye. Mrs. Dashwood, Margaret, Elinor, and Marianne are picked up and carried like so much furniture and deposited in their new home. Marianne carries a basket which occasionally emits a plaintive meow. They survey the cottage, surrounded by their belongings.

The Cottage

MARGARET. It's so small!

MARIANNE. Margaret.

ELINOR. It will fit all of us comfortably, and Thomas and Betsy. We are really very fortunate, dear.

MARGARET. Where shall I put my telescope?

MARIANNE. Next to my pianoforte. You may spy on the neighbors!

ELINOR. Marianne.

MARIANNE. …You may not spy on the neighbors.

MRS. DASHWOOD. It is rather small, but I am sure that we will soon have plenty of money, and then we may think about building!

SIR JOHN. *(From outside the cottage.)* Hallllloooo!

MRS. JENNINGS. *(Echoing.)* Halllooooooooo, halllooooo!

Sir John Middleton and Mrs. Jennings sweep in—they don't stop moving the whole time. Sir John is a boisterous middle-aged man; Mrs. Jennings, his even more boisterous mother-in-law.

She has a herd of noisy lapdogs—represented by the Gossips, yapping like dogs throughout. It is a circus. They constantly interrupt each other and overlap portions of lines throughout.

SIR JOHN. Mrs. Dashwood! Welcome, welcome! May I present my mother-in-law, Mrs. Jennings?

MRS. JENNINGS. Hallo, how d'ye do? Always so thrilling to meet a relation! Excuse these noisy devils, they get over-excited. Hush!

MRS. DASHWOOD. Sir John. My daughters, Elinor, Marianne, and Margaret.

SIR JOHN. *(To Mrs. Jennings.)* Have you ever seen prettier girls in all the world? *(To the dogs.)* HUSH, HUSH, YOU!

MRS. JENNINGS. I am sure they have left many broken young gentlemen in Devonshire! HUSH!

    Marianne is repulsed.

SIR JOHN. You must, of course, dine at Barton Park every day until you are settled. HUSH!

    Mrs. Dashwood opens her mouth to politely refuse. The dog barking reaches a crescendo.

MRS. JENNINGS. Come! You must come! HUSH! We shall not leave until you agree to come—HUSH!	SIR JOHN. Come, come! You must come!

MRS. DASHWOOD. We shall wait on you for dinner, if it is no inconvenience.

SIR JOHN. Lady Middleton will be so pleased. We expect you tonight!	MRS. JENNINGS. Oh, she shall be frantic with excitement!
MRS. JENNINGS. Tonight! HUSH! HUSH!	SIR JOHN. The prettiest girls in all England! HUSH!

    They sweep off as quickly as they swept on. Before the Dash-woods have any time to recover, the Barton Park dining table is wheeled on, fully set, and they are ushered in by Sir John. Mrs. Jennings and Lady Middleton [Sir John's very overbred wife] sit. Sir John talks over. As he speaks, he introduces Colonel Brandon—an older, wealthy bachelor.

SIR JOHN. I must apologize to you, Miss Elinor and Miss Marianne, I was unable to get any eligible young bachelors here tonight. Only our particular friend, Colonel Brandon—but he is neither young nor very gay, I'm afraid. Brandon, old boy, come and feast your eyes upon Miss Elinor and Marianne Dashwood!

> *Brandon starts upon meeting Marianne and stares at her, not bowing.*

Brandon.

> *Brandon recalls himself and bows.*

Aren't they the most charming girls in all England? To dinner, to dinner! I only hope you will not find it so very dull!

Barton Park

> *They sit. Midway through dinner. Mrs. Jennings and Sir John are exceedingly loud and boisterous.*

MRS. JENNINGS. Miss Margaret, surely *you* can tell us the name of the young man who is Miss Elinor's particular favorite in Sussex?

> *Pause as Margaret considers this.*

MARGARET. I must not tell, may I, Elinor?

MARIANNE. Margaret. Remember that whatever conjectures you may have, you have no right to repeat them!

MARGARET. I never had any conjectures about it, it was you who told me of it yourself.

> *Marianne discreetly stomps on her foot under the table.*

Ow!

> *This increases the mirth of the company.*

MRS. JENNINGS. Pray, Miss Margaret, let us know all about it. What is the gentleman's name?

MARGARET. I must not tell, ma'am. But I know very well what it is; and I know where he is too.

MRS. JENNINGS. We can guess where he is; in Norland to be sure. He is the curate of the parish, I dare say?

MARGARET. He is of no profession at all.

MARIANNE. Margaret, you know that this is all your own invention, and that there is no such person in existence.

MARGARET. Well, then, he is lately dead, Marianne, for I am sure there was such a man once, and his name begins with an F.

MRS. JENNINGS. F! F, F, F.   SIR JOHN. F, hey? F-f-f-f!

COL. BRANDON. *(Heroically creating a diversion.)* It…has rained very hard recently. It has rained every day for the last fortnight, I believe. *(To Lady Middleton.)* Do you not find the weather unusually inclement of late, ma'am?

LADY MIDDLETON. Rain. Shocking. Rain.

COL. BRANDON. Yes. It has been a very wet spring.

MARIANNE. Margaret, please be so good as to join me at the pianoforte.

MARGARET. Why?…

> *Marianne pinches her beneath the table.*

Owww!

MRS. JENNINGS. Ohhhh, Miss Marianne, d'you play?

> *Marianne, by way of an answer, flips open the piano covering rather loudly.*

ELINOR. Please do excuse my sister's…enthusiasm.

SIR JOHN. No, pound away, by all means!

MRS. JENNINGS. Yes, we are all prepared to be charmed!

LADY MIDDLETON. Very fond. Of. Music.

> *Marianne sings very simply and plays the piano.* Colonel Brandon stands watching Marianne. He is deeply, though not ostentatiously, affected. The rest of the party continues to chatter to each other, oblivious to the music. The Gossips drift in and listen—Mrs. Jennings turns suddenly and speaks to them.*

MRS. JENNINGS. Oh, Colonel Brandon is VERY much in love with Miss Marianne Dashwood! I rather suspected it to be so, on the

---

* In the original off-Broadway run, Marianne sang a portion of "Polwart on the Green," a simple song in the public domain—which happens to be in Jane Austen's personal songbook. It's a nice touch, but not mandatory.

first evening they met, from his listening while she sang; and on the second visit, when he listened to her sing *again*! It is an excellent match, for HE is rich, and SHE is handsome—and I am sure he need not wait any longer!

GOSSIP 4. Colonel Brandon is a VERY eligible bachelor!

GOSSIP 2. A bit long in the tooth—why, my Cassandra set her cap at him, and that was ten years ago!

GOSSIP 3. Oooh, that great big property he inherited! I cannot think of it but I am breathless!

GOSSIP 4. Such a sober man—a young woman's touch would liven him up!

GOSSIP 2. A young pretty woman—either breathe life into him or kill him within a fortnight!

MRS. JENNINGS. A match, a match, a perfect match! I will find a good husband for every decent girl in the county, mark my words!

> *Marianne abruptly stops playing, distracted, and breaks through the chattering Gossips.*

Marianne and Love

> *The Dashwoods' drawing room. Elinor and Mrs. Dashwood sit, embroidering.*

MARIANNE. Colonel Brandon is nearly old enough to be my father, and if he was ever animated enough to be in love, has long outlived the sensation. When is a man to be safe from such wit, if age and infirmity do not protect him?

ELINOR. Infirmity! Do you call Colonel Brandon infirm?

MARIANNE. Yesterday he spoke of his flannel waistcoat!

ELINOR. …And?

MARIANNE. A flannel waistcoat for his aching joints! The commonest signifier of declining life!

MRS. DASHWOOD. My dearest child, if you estimate the colonel thus, I imagine you must be in continual terror of MY decay. It must seem to you a miracle that I still live.

MARIANNE. Mamma, you are not doing me justice. I know that Colonel Brandon is not in any danger of immediate expiration; he may live twenty years longer. But a man of his age should have nothing to do with matrimony.

ELINOR. Perhaps a man of his age and a lady of your age should not have anything to do with matrimony together. But if there were a woman who was single at thirty, I do not think anyone would object to the colonel marrying HER.

MARIANNE. A woman of thirty can never hope to feel or inspire affection again. If her fortune is small, I suppose that she might bring herself to be a nurse, for the security of being a wife.

ELINOR. Must you doom Colonel Brandon to a slow decline because he happened to complain of an ache in his shoulder? If he had been in a violent fever, you would not despise him half so much. Confess, Marianne, is not there something *thrilling* to you in the flushed cheek, hollow eye, and quick pulse of a fever?

THOMAS. Ma'am, Lord Middleton is here to ask if you have any letters to post.

SIR JOHN. *(From outside.)* Hallloooo!

ELINOR. I will take them.

    Elinor exits.

MARIANNE. Margaret, will you go and get your boots on?

MARGARET. We're not still going for a walk, are we? It is goiiiiiing to raiiiiiin!

MARIANNE. No, it is not. Now go and get your boots, please.

MARGARET. Oh, boots. Boots boots boots!

    Margaret exits.

MARIANNE. Mamma, I have had an alarum on the subject of sickness, which I must share with you. I am sure that Edward Ferrars is not well!

MRS. DASHWOOD. Oh?

MARIANNE. We have been here almost a fortnight, and he has not yet come. What else but grave illness could be keeping him away?

MRS. DASHWOOD. Does Elinor expect him?

MARIANNE. She must!

MRS. DASHWOOD. She has said nothing to me.

MARIANNE. It is all so strange! Do you know—I purposely left them alone together twice on our last morning at Norland, and each time he most unaccountably followed me out of the room!

Margaret reenters.

MRS. DASHWOOD. *(To Marianne.)* Shh.

MARGARET. …What?

Elinor reenters.

ELINOR. Are you still walking? It looks as though it is going to rain.

MARGARET. Mariaaaaaanne!

MARIANNE. All this talk of a wet spring! It is NOT GOING TO RAIN, the day will be everlastingly fair! NOW COME ALONG!

They exit, Margaret dragging her feet.

Marianne's Gallant Preserver

Some time passes—pouring rain is heard. Elinor and Mrs. Dashwood sit and sew.

ELINOR. A very wet spring. We should tell Betsy to put on tea—they will be soaked through.

MARGARET. *(Runs in, breathless.)* Elinor! Mamma! Marianne fell! And hurt her ankle! And a gentleman! Grabbed her right up!

MRS. DASHWOOD. Margaret, what on earth—

MARGARET. *(Excitedly pointing.)* Marianne's preserver! Marianne's preserver!

Willoughby enters, carrying Marianne, who is deeply embarrassed by his hands on her—she can't even look at him. He is uncommonly handsome, a classic Romantic hero.

Marianne's preserver!

28

WILLOUGHBY. Please forgive my intrusion, ma'am; the lady took a tumble, and was not able to stand.

He places Marianne on the couch and turns to speak to Mrs. Dashwood; while he does this, Marianne raises her head and makes frantic faces at Elinor.

MRS. DASHWOOD. Margaret, run and tell Betsy what has happened. Marianne, dearest, are you in much pain?

Marianne shakes her head. Margaret, transfixed, doesn't leave.

WILLOUGHBY. Only a wrenched ankle, I think.

MRS. DASHWOOD. Thank heavens you were there. Please, sir— will you sit and take some tea?

WILLOUGHBY. I am dirty and wet, and do not want to spoil your furniture.

ELINOR. *(At Marianne's frantic prompting.)* Might I ask to whom we are so obliged?

WILLOUGHBY. My name is John Willoughby. I hope, ma'am, you will allow me the honor of calling tomorrow to enquire after Miss…

MRS. DASHWOOD. Dashwood. *(Tries to recall herself.)* Is our name. I am Mrs. Dashwood. This is Elinor, Margaret, and—

MARIANNE. *(Boldly.)* —Miss Marianne Dashwood.

Willoughby takes Marianne's hand and bows, looking directly into her eyes.

MRS. DASHWOOD. You will be very welcome, Mr. Willoughby. Will you not wait for the rain to clear?

WILLOUGHBY. Thank you, ma'am, but my pointers are outside. A little more water will not melt me.

The ladies giggle giddily at his joke.

Until tomorrow.

He departs. There is a moment of awed silence.

MARGARET. Marianne's gallant preserver!

Willoughby in the County

The next morning. Margaret drags Sir John into the room, regaling him.

MARGARET. ...And then Mamma asked him whether he would sit down, but he would not, as he was so muddy and dirty, but he is to call again today!

MRS. DASHWOOD. Do you know any gentleman by the name of Willoughby?

SIR JOHN. Willoughby! What, is he in the county? He is down here every spring. I must ask him to dinner on Thursday.

MRS. DASHWOOD. And what sort of a young man is he?

SIR JOHN. As good a fellow as ever lived! Not a bolder rider in England.

ELINOR. And where is his residence?

SIR JOHN. Mr. Willoughby has no property of his own in this county; he resides here only while visiting his rich old cousin, Mrs. Smith, at Allenham Court. He's to inherit the estate and all her fortune, eventually!

ELINOR. Oh!

SIR JOHN. He is very well worth catching, Miss Dashwood; and if I were you, I would not give him up so easily to my younger sister. Miss Marianne must not expect to have all the men to herself! Brandon will be jealous, if she does not take care!

MRS. DASHWOOD. *(Heading off Marianne's outraged objection.)* My daughters, Sir John, have not been brought up to "catch" gentlemen. I am glad to hear, however, that he is a respectable young man.

MARIANNE. Of course he is *respectable*, Mamma!

SIR JOHN. Aye, I see how it is! You will be setting your cap at him now, and never think of poor Brandon. How can he compete against all this tumbling about and spraining of ankles?

Willoughby Visits the Dashwoods

Willoughby sits with Marianne, Elinor, and Mrs. Dashwood. Marianne's foot is propped up.

MARIANNE. Cowper!

WILLOUGHBY. Yes. I daresay that Scott or Pope is a more serious-minded answer, but I am afraid that Cowper is my favorite poet of our time.

MARIANNE. Cowper may indeed be the greatest poet of *any* time. Pray, what is your favorite poem, Mr. Willoughby? Mine must be "Hope."

ELINOR. I think—

WILLOUGHBY. *(Interrupting, quoting "Hope.")*
   —Oh, see me sworn to serve thee, and command
   A painter's skill into a poet's hand!

MARIANNE.
   That, while I, trembling, trace a work divine
   Fancy may stand aloof from the design,

WILLOUGHBY.	MARIANNE.
And light, and shade, and ev'ry stroke, be thine.	And light, and shade, and ev'ry stroke, be thine.

   Pause.

MRS. DASHWOOD. Mr. Willoughby, won't you join us for dinner?

WILLOUGHBY. I beg your pardon, ma'am, but I must dine with my cousin at Allenham. I had no idea it was so late. Might I enquire after Miss Marianne again tomorrow?

MRS. DASHWOOD. By all means.

MARIANNE. Until tomorrow.

   He bows to the ladies and exits.

ELINOR. Well, Marianne! Nobody can ever accuse you of being too reserved.

MARIANNE. You are right, Elinor. I have been too much at ease, too happy, too frank. I have been open and sincere when I ought to have been spiritless and dull! I suppose you think I should have talked solely of the weather, and the roads, and only spoken once every ten minutes—or better yet, never spoken at all?

MRS. DASHWOOD. My love, she is only teasing you. Elinor, surely we would never wish to check Marianne's conversations with her *(Significantly.)* new friend.

Marianne's Future

GOSSIP 3. A love match indeed!

GOSSIP 2. I hear that Mr. Willoughby visits the Dashwoods every day.

GOSSIP 4. Scooping her up in the driving rain!

GOSSIP 1. Add a horde of gypsies and you'd have a penny novel.

GOSSIP 3. Married within a month, mark my words!

GOSSIP 1. He has no money to marry! Depends entirely on that old cousin.

GOSSIP 4. But when he inherits from her, they will be wealthy indeed! Wealthy and handsome—what more could one wish?

GOSSIP 2. Look at them, no eyes for anyone else in the world...

Marianne stands and faces the Gossips directly, recklessly.

MARIANNE. This is indeed the season of my happiness!

GOSSIP 3. But what of poor Colonel Brandon?

MARIANNE. Colonel Brandon! Colonel Brandon and his wet spring!

A Very Wet Spring

Willoughby, Marianne, and Elinor amuse themselves on the lawn at Barton Park.

WILLOUGHBY. Colonel Brandon is the kind of man everybody speaks well of, and who nobody cares about.

Marianne giggles at his badness.

ELINOR. Why should you dislike him?

MARIANNE. Why should you like him?

ELINOR. He is very civil. He has seen a great deal of the world, and always answers my inquiries with good breeding and good nature.

MARIANNE. That is to say he has told you that in the East Indies the climate is hot, and the mosquitoes are troublesome!

ELINOR. You are both unfair to him, and it is not witty in either of you.

WILLOUGHBY. Oho! In defence of your protégé, Miss Dashwood, you can even be saucy!

ELINOR. My protégé, as you call him, is a sensible man, and sense will always have attractions for me. Yes, Marianne, even in a man over forty.

WILLOUGHBY. Oh, he is very respectable! As respectable as a statue or a monument, our terrible stiff perfectly inhuman colonel. I'm amazed he can still bend at the waist.

> *He struts around imitating Brandon's stiff walk. Marianne giggles again.*

ELINOR. *(Rather stiffly herself.)* Well. I have always found him to be a perfect gentleman.

WILLOUGHBY. ...But not me?

MARIANNE. Elinor!

WILLOUGHBY. No, no—I fear she is only too right. Miss Dashwood, forgive me. In utter self-reproach, I cast myself at your feet. To once again bask in the light of your sweet approbation, I surrender my case entirely. I, John Willoughby, confess that Colonel Brandon's character is completely and entirely irreproachable! And yet, somehow, I dislike him as much as ever.

> *Colonel Brandon approaches.*

Speak of the devil...

MARIANNE. Oh, we are never safe from him!

WILLOUGHBY. You have poor timing, Brandon—I was just about to take Miss Marianne to look at the greenhouse. There are some very interesting orchids there.

MARIANNE. Orchids? Yes, we must go look at the...orchids. I so adore an orchid. Please do excuse us, Colonel.

They leave, barely keeping their laughter in check.

COL. BRANDON. *(Still watching her.)* Your sister is full of life.

ELINOR. She is certainly...energetic. Some day her disposition will settle. I hope.

COL. BRANDON. I am sorry to think of her ever changing.

ELINOR. I cannot agree with you there. Marianne's ideals are all very romantic, but they tend to discard propriety entirely. She would benefit from a more mature understanding of certain realities.

COL. BRANDON. Do not desire it too much. I once knew a lady who resembled your sister—and her introduction to what you might call "realities" was very unfortunate. I will not trouble you with the story. Pardon me—have you dropped this?

He picks her handkerchief off the ground.

ELINOR. Oh, yes.

COL. BRANDON. Shall I have it laundered?

ELINOR. *(Rather more frantic than is necessary.)* No! No, thank you.

COL. BRANDON. I beg your pardon. But you see, it is covered with ink.

*Elinor shakes her head. Mortified, she snatches back the hand-
kerchief. Marianne rushes back on, flushed with excitement.
Elinor balls Edward's handkerchief up in her hand.*

MARIANNE. *(All sweetness.)* Colonel Brandon, please excuse me. May I steal my sister's attention for a moment?

Brandon bows and walks away.

Elinor, I have the most wonderful news. Willoughby has given me a horse!

ELINOR. A horse!

MARIANNE. One which is exactly bred to carry a woman! He is sending his groom for it immediately!

ELINOR. Marianne, you cannot accept such a present.

MARIANNE. Why not? Elinor, we shall share its use!

ELINOR. A horse! From a strange man!

MARIANNE. What "strange man?" We are speaking of Willoughby!

ELINOR. And he is very little known to you! *(This is too much.)*

MARIANNE. I may not have been acquainted with Willoughby for long, Elinor—but I know him much better than I know any other creature in the world! Except you and Mamma, of course.

ELINOR. Marianne—let us not touch upon the impropriety, for a moment. We cannot afford to keep a horse.

MARIANNE. Surely we could find the money!

ELINOR. We have enough to do just to keep ourselves respectable.

MARIANNE. …There must be some way.

ELINOR. …We must go in for dinner.

Brandon's Letter

The party assembles for dinner at Barton Park.

MARIANNE. *(Looking at Elinor pointedly.)* Mr. Willoughby, I must speak to you about your kind offer.

> *She draws him aside and speaks low to him, although Elinor stays close enough that they are not alone.*

WILLOUGHBY. But, Marianne!

> *Elinor starts at the use of Marianne's Christian name. Marianne whispers again to him. They both giggle, looking at Elinor, who is excluded.*

Queen Mab is still yours, Marianne. I shall keep her only till you can claim her for your more *lasting* home.

> *He takes her hand and kisses it. Marianne beams at him and walks into the dinner with him. Elinor is left alone with Edward's handkerchief, which she looks at for a moment before she follows them. Dinner with Mrs. Jennings, Lady Middleton, Sir John, and Colonel Brandon. Lively overlapping conversation.* The servant comes in, bearing a letter, which is presented to Colonel Brandon. He looks at the handwriting, starts out of his chair, and leaves the room.*

---

* See appendix for additional text that may be used to create the overlapping conversations.

SIR JOHN. What is the matter with Brandon?

LADY MIDDLETON. He left. My. Dinner table.

Colonel Brandon reenters.

MRS. JENNINGS. No bad news, Colonel, I hope.

COL. BRANDON. None at all, ma'am.

MRS. JENNINGS. But what was that letter?

COL. BRANDON. Merely a letter of business.

MRS. JENNINGS. Then how did it discompose you so much? Come, let us hear the truth of it. Oh, oh! I know who it is from. And I hope she is well.

COL. BRANDON. Whom do you mean, ma'am?

MRS. JENNINGS. Oh, you know who.

COL. BRANDON. *(Turning again to Lady Middleton.)* I am very sorry, ma'am, that I received this tonight. I am afraid that it requires my immediate attendance in town—

MRS. JENNINGS. What can you have to do in town at this time of year?—   SIR JOHN. In town!

COL. BRANDON. —and I do not mean to break up the party, but I am afraid that I must depart this moment.

SIR JOHN. Tonight?! Absurd! Go tomorrow instead!

COL. BRANDON. I regret that I cannot.

WILLOUGHBY. *(To Marianne, not quietly enough.)* There are some people who cannot bear a party of pleasure. I would lay fifty guineas that Brandon invented this trick to get out of our gathering.

MARIANNE. I have no doubt of it.

SIR JOHN. This is all very unorthodox.

MRS. JENNINGS. Well, when will you come back again?

COL. BRANDON. I dare not say.

SERVANT. Your horses are ready, sir.

SIR JOHN. You had better change your mind!

COL. BRANDON. It is not in my power. Might I see you and your sisters in London this winter, Miss Dashwood?

ELINOR. I am afraid not.

COL. BRANDON. Then I must bid you farewell for a longer time than I should wish. *(Bowing to Elinor, then Marianne.)* Miss Marianne.

MRS. JENNINGS. Colonel, before you go—do let us know what you are going about!

COL. BRANDON. Good evening, ma'am.

He leaves the room, accompanied by Sir John.

WILLOUGHBY. How provoking!

MRS. JENNINGS. I can guess what his business is…it is about Miss Williams, I am sure.

MARIANNE. And who is Miss Williams?

MRS. JENNINGS. She is a relation of the colonel's, my dear; a very near relation. I will not say how near, for fear of shocking you. *(To Elinor—at a stage whisper which is precisely the same volume—)* She is his *natural daughter.*

ELINOR. Indeed!

MRS. JENNINGS. And as like him as she can stare. It was the great scandal of the county fifteen-odd years ago. The mother died, I understand, although we never could get all of the details. He is very fond of the little love-child; I dare say he will leave her all his fortune.

WILLOUGHBY. A love-child from old prim-and-proper Brandon! What a first-rate hypocrite!

Mrs. Jennings hushes him. Sir John returns.

MRS. JENNINGS. Did Brandon give you any further intelligence?

SIR JOHN. No; I suppose it must be something he is ashamed of. Well, despite our reduced numbers, we must make ourselves merry. What do you all say to a ramble after dinner? A short, moonlit drive about the country?

MRS. JENNINGS. Ask Mr. Willoughby and Miss Marianne about *drives in the country!*

MARIANNE. Ma'am?

MRS. JENNINGS. I have found you out in spite of all your tricks. This morning, when we all went driving, and you two sped away out of sight? I made my woman enquire of your groom, sir, and I know where you spent the morning!

WILLOUGHBY. Yes, out in my carriage.

MRS. JENNINGS. Yes, yes, Mr. Impudence, and I found out WHERE you went in that carriage. *(Same too-loud stage whisper.)* I hope you like your future house, Miss Marianne, and I look forward to visiting you at Allenham!

SIR JOHN. A good trick on us! Willoughby, tell me, have you still got that fine mare?

> *The conversation fades; the ensemble rises from the table as the Gossips clear. Later. Elinor turns in horror to her sister and pulls her aside as they leave the dining room.*

ELINOR. Marianne, did you really visit Allenham with Mr. Willoughby?

MARIANNE. Yes.

ELINOR. With no companion other than Mr. Willoughby?

MARIANNE. We did not do anything wrong, Elinor! Mr. Willoughby has a perfect right to shew that estate. It will all one day belong to him!

ELINOR. Even if Allenham was one day to belong to YOU, Marianne, you would not be justified in what you have done.

MARIANNE. *(Rather more pleased than offended.)* Elinor!

ELINOR. Why didn't you tell me?

MARIANNE. Why don't you talk to me about Edward?

ELINOR. …There is nothing to tell.

MARIANNE. Well, the same is true for me! There was nothing to tell really, Elinor. We took a little stroll!

> *Pause.*

Perhaps it WAS rather ill-judged in me to go without a chaperon or a formal invitation, but Willoughby wanted particularly to shew me privately; there is the sweetest little garden there, and a sitting room just so…

> *Marianne's chatter fades into the background, as the Gossips speak over.*

GOSSIP 2. No news of an engagement yet?

GOSSIP 3. I cannot think why—he uses her Christian name quite openly!

GOSSIP 2. Such an extraordinary silence!

GOSSIP 1. An establishment may not be within his power, until he inherits.

GOSSIP 4. He certainly lives expensively.

GOSSIP 5. All fashion and no fortune, as they say!

GOSSIP 3. But no announcement of their attachment yet?

GOSSIP 4. Why such secrecy?

GOSSIP 2. Why such secrecy?!

GOSSIP 1. Why such secrecy?!

A Sad Goodbye

Elinor, Mrs. Dashwood, and Margaret walk on the lane.

MARGARET. *(Dancing around.)* I have such a secret to tell you both about Marianne! I am sure she will be married to Mr. Willoughby very soon.

ELINOR. You have said that almost every day since they met, Margaret.

MARGARET. But indeed now I am sure they will be married very soon, for he has got a lock of her hair.

Mrs. Dashwood and Elinor exchange glances.

ELINOR. How do you know?

MARGARET. I know MANY secrets, Elinor.

ELINOR. Margaret.

MARGARET. I saw him take it! Last night after tea, when you and Mamma went out of the room, they were whispering together, and he took up her scissors and cut off a lock of her hair, and he kissed it, and put it into his pocketbook! And today she asked to stay at home, ALONE… I am sure that he must be visiting with her now!

MRS. DASHWOOD. *(Half-heartedly chiding.)* Margaret…

They arrive back at the cottage.

MARGARET. It is Mr. Willoughby's curricle outside! I told you, he DID visit her!

Suddenly, Marianne rushes past them, sobbing.

ELINOR. Marianne?!

Marianne is gone. Alarmed, they continue into the parlor. Willoughby stands with his back to them.

MRS. DASHWOOD. Mr. Willoughby?

WILLOUGHBY. *(Not turning around.)* Good day.

MRS. DASHWOOD. Is anything amiss?

WILLOUGHBY. Yes. There has been…a very heavy disappointment. I am afraid I am unable to picnick with you today.

Awkward pause.

MRS. DASHWOOD. Well, then, perhaps tomorrow!

WILLOUGHBY. Mrs. Smith has commanded her poor dependent cousin to conduct some business for her in London, right away. I have just received my marching orders, and must leave immediately.

MRS. DASHWOOD. …Her business will not keep you from us long, I hope?

WILLOUGHBY. You are very kind, but I do not think I can return to Devonshire soon. Mrs. Smith will not have me more than once a year.

ELINOR. And is Allenham the only house in the neighborhood in which you are welcome? For shame, Willoughby, do you need a formal invitation to visit us here?

WILLOUGHBY. …You are too good. My engagements at present… are of such a nature—

He comes to an awkward halt.

It is folly to linger. I will not torment myself by remaining any longer!

Willoughby leaves without bowing. Pause.

ELINOR. Margaret, will you please go and tell Betsy that Marianne won't be coming down for dinner?

MARGARET. But—

ELINOR. Please, dear.

Margaret, disappointed on missing out, leaves.

Do you think that they have quarreled?

MRS. DASHWOOD. Oh, Elinor. Why do you always love to think the worst?

ELINOR. *(Stung.)* I don't. But what else could have happened?

MRS. DASHWOOD. Why, it is perfectly obvious. I can account for everything.

ELINOR. Can you?

MRS. DASHWOOD. Yes! Mrs. Smith must have invented this business in London as an excuse to send Willoughby away. Word has finally reached her of the attachment between Willoughby and Marianne; she disapproves and strives to separate them. Because he is dependent on her, he dares not confess to her—yet—that they are already engaged, and must obey her wishes—for a time! And that is why he cannot predict when he will return. Elinor—what say you?

ELINOR. Nothing. You may be right, Mamma.

MRS. DASHWOOD. Your countenance suggests that you think otherwise. What are your conjectures?

ELINOR. I do not mean to cast suspicion. But Mamma—it may indeed be prudent to conceal their engagement from Mrs. Smith, but why do they conceal it from us?

MRS. DASHWOOD. His entire behavior to Marianne declares that he considers her as his future wife!

ELINOR. My doubts may soon be done away. If they write to each other, they are obviously engaged.

MRS. DASHWOOD. A mighty concession indeed! Ungracious girl. If you were to see them at the altar, would you *then* admit they were going to be married?

ELINOR. Perhaps we should ask Marianne directly if she is engaged?

MRS. DASHWOOD. You may do as you like, but I would find it very ungenerous to ever force such a confidence! I would not ask that question for the world. Marianne shall tell me what she will, when she will, however she sees fit!

MARGARET. *(Reenters.)* I have told Betsy; she wants to know if she should send Marianne's dinner up?

MRS. DASHWOOD. Let us practice your French, dear.

MARGARET. …Nobody ever tells me anything.

The Visit

Several weeks later. Marianne, very depressed, puts on her shawl to go for a walk.

ELINOR. Marianne, are you going for a walk? Shall I join you?

MARIANNE. Where would you like to go?

ELINOR. On the downs?

MARIANNE. I am sorry, Elinor. I meant to go on the lanes.

ELINOR. Marianne, please. For weeks, you have avoided everybody. Will you take the air with me, once?

Pause. Marianne nods. They walk.

The sky is very beautiful today.

No response.

We never finished reading *Marchmont*, Marianne.

No response.

Perhaps we could put it aside until Willoughby rejoins us—but it may be many months before that happens.

MARIANNE. Months! No—nor many weeks.

ELINOR. Indeed? Marianne, have you and Willoughby—

MARIANNE. Elinor! Who is that?

She runs to the lane. Elinor follows.

ELINOR. Is it Colonel Brandon?

MARIANNE. No—

ELINOR.	MARIANNE. *(With rising excitement.)*
Is it Willoughby?	No, no—Elinor, look, LOOK!

MARIANNE. *(Waves with great enthusiasm.)* Hello, hello! It is us, yes, hello!

Edward Ferrars enters, possibly leading a Gossip playing a horse.

ELINOR. Mr. Ferrars!

EDWARD. Miss Dashwood. Miss Marianne.

MARIANNE. Edward! Oh, Edward! Good God, what on earth could have taken you so long?!

Her wild enthusiasm is embarrassing for both Elinor and Edward; he awkwardly sticks out a hand for her to shake. She does so, enthusiastically, then looks expectantly at Elinor, who very awkwardly shakes Edward's hand. They both drop the handshake immediately.

EDWARD. Yes. Hello. Hello! I am very pleased to see you both.

MARIANNE. Indeed, this is almost the greatest happiness imaginable! Have you come directly from Norland?

EDWARD. No. I have been in Devonshire a fortnight, and now come purposely to visit you.

MARIANNE. Edward, you have been in the county a fortnight without visiting us?

EDWARD. *(Lamely.)* I have been visiting some friends near Plymouth.

MARIANNE. Well, come. Welcome!

Laughs a little at her own lame joke.

Walk back with us! Mamma will be so happy to FINALLY see you! *(Transparently trying to leave them alone.)* Or perhaps I should just run ahead and tell her that you are coming!

As she starts to run:

EDWARD. Marianne, wait. Perhaps we should all just...walk together.

Edward in Barton Park

Marianne, Elinor, and Margaret walk Edward into tea at Barton Park. Mrs. Dashwood, Mrs. Jennings, Lady Middleton, and Sir John all join.

MRS. DASHWOOD. Sir John, Mrs. Jennings, may I present Mr. Edward Ferrars.

MRS. JENNINGS. Oh, Mr. F-f-fffffferrars! *(With great emphasis on the "f," turning meaningfully to Sir John.)*

SIR JOHN. Ah, Mr. F-f-f-ferrars!

MRS. JENNINGS. What an unspeakable pleasure to meet you, Mr. F-f-ferrars!

ELINOR. *(Trying to change the subject.)* Would anyone care for some tea?

MRS. DASHWOOD. I would, certainly.   MARIANNE. Please.

SIR JOHN. F-f-ferrars!

MARIANNE. *(Trying AGAIN to change the subject.)* I never saw you wear a ring before, Edward. Is it new?

EDWARD. Yes. No. It is old, that is, but new to me. Recent. Have I never worn it before? Yes.

He may ineffectually try to hide the hand.

SIR JOHN. Mr. Ferrars—

MRS. JENNINGS. Long F, sir, long F!

SIR JOHN. Mr. Fffffferrars, you MUST have dinner with us tomorrow night, for we shall be quite alone—and the night after you must absolutely dine with us again, for we shall be a large party.

MRS. JENNINGS. And perhaps we may raise a dance in the next week! How long shall we have you in our corner of England, Mr. Ferrars? We are quite bereft of eligible young bachelors here! However long you remain a bachelor, that is!

LADY MIDDLETON. *(Reprovingly.)* Mother.

EDWARD. I am afraid I am only staying tonight, ma'am.

MARGARET. Noooooooooooooo!

SIR JOHN. *(Very surprised.)* A lot of riding for such a short visit.

MARIANNE. Only for tonight, Edward?

MRS. JENNINGS. *(Significantly, looking at Elinor.)* Oho, I see. I suppose you only came for some particular errand?

SIR JOHN. Oh, I see!

EDWARD. I…I was in the county, ma'am.

SIR JOHN. Well, whatever your reason, we must have you stay longer now!

MRS. JENNINGS. Yes, young man. Do not be a ninny.

SIR JOHN. Stay.

MRS. JENNINGS. Stay!

SIR JOHN. Stay!

MRS. JENNINGS. Stay!

MRS. DASHWOOD. Edward, really, you are more than welcome.

SIR JOHN. STAY!

MRS. JENNINGS. STAY!

MARGARET. *(Plaintively.)* ...Stay?

> *Pause.*

EDWARD. ...I am afraid I must attend my mother.

> *Pause.*

SIR JOHN. Truly, Mr. Ferrars, such a very short visit...

LADY MIDDLETON. Why. Come. At all.

> *Silence. They rise. The Dashwoods and Edward walk back to the cottage.*

Edward Takes His Leave

MARIANNE. Really, Edward—it's too ridiculous. You must stay!

EDWARD. I am sorry beyond what I can say, but I must go to my mother.

MRS. DASHWOOD. Well. *(Switching the subject.)* And what are Mrs. Ferrars' aims for you at present, Edward?

EDWARD. Much the same. I am to rise high in the world, but I must have no profession—that would be too common. Given the choice, I should like to find employment in the church—but it is not smart enough for my family. And so my own nicety, and the nicety of my relations turns me into what I am: an idle, helpless being.

MRS. DASHWOOD. Come, Edward. Such melancholy! Your mother will give you, in time, the financial independence you are so anxious for. How much good may not a few months do?

EDWARD. I think that I may defy many months to produce any good to me. *"What is a man, if his chief good and market of his time/ Be but to sleep and feed? A beast, no more."*—That's from *Hamlet*, Marianne, but perhaps you didn't recognize it, because my delivery is so improved? Forgive me if I am very saucy.

45

MARIANNE. I love to be reminded of the past, Edward, and you will never offend me by talking of it.

EDWARD. And do you feel so strongly about Hamlet's beating heart as you once did?

MARIANNE. At my time of life, opinions are fixed. It is not likely that I should now ever change them.

ELINOR. Marianne is as steadfast as ever.

EDWARD. She is only grown a little more grave.

MARIANNE. Nay, Edward, you need not reproach me. You are not very gay yourself.

EDWARD. No, I suppose not.

MARIANNE. But worse, you are reserved.

EDWARD. Reserved?

MARIANNE. *(Pointedly.)* Yes, very.

EDWARD. What do you mean?

ELINOR. Marianne thinks everybody reserved who is not quite so open as she is. *(Switching the subject.)* And here we are at last!

> *They arrive at the cottage.*

MRS. DASHWOOD. Well, Edward. I suppose we must bid you adieu. Do you know when you may return?

EDWARD. I cannot say.

MARIANNE. Please do come again soon, Edward—please.

> *She presses his hand. Margaret hugs him. Marianne and her mother look significantly at Edward and Elinor as they go inside, pulling Margaret along with them. Elinor stands at the gate, uncertain—should she stay? Is he going to ask her anything? There is a pause. They stand looking at each other.*

EDWARD. Miss Dashwood.

> *He bows and leaves.*

Meet the Steeles

Elinor, humiliated and confused, sits and attempts to occupy herself at her drawing table.* The next morning. Sir John and Mrs. Jennings approach the cottage, with the Steeles (two young sisters from the lower-middle class) in tow. The Steeles wait outside politely.

SIR JOHN.	MRS. JENNINGS.
Hullo, hullo Miss Dashwood!	Hullo, Miss Dashwood!

MRS. JENNINGS. Where is Miss Marianne? Has she run away because we are come?

ELINOR. She is out walking.

SIR JOHN. Well, lay that work aside for one moment, Lady Industry: I have brought you some strangers! Miss Anne and Lucy Steele, who are to stay with us at the Park. How do you like them?

ELINOR. Hush! They will hear you!

MRS. JENNINGS. I met them on a morning's excursion to Exeter, and discovered them to be my relations! Yes, the cousins of my cousin Mildred's own Mr. John—nay, not you, sir, a shorter and fuller man, if you please. Very gouty, poor fellow, and never comfortable in the least bit of damp. Where was I?

ELINOR. Your relations, ma'am.

MRS. JENNINGS. Yes, can you imagine? Naturally we invited them to stay with us directly! I daresay you can see the resemblance?

SIR JOHN. They are the sweetest girls in the world! You must come for a visit tonight, you can't think how you will like them!

MRS. JENNINGS.	SIR JOHN.
Come, come, come, come!	Come, come!

Sir John and Mrs. Jennings pull Lucy Steele and Anne Steele to sit in the parlor, and then push Elinor and Marianne on, as if positioning puppets. Marianne tries to make a break for it; Elinor pulls her down into her chair. An awkward silence.

---

* See note in appendix, page 96.

Visit with the Steeles

LUCY. What a lovely room this is! So very well-appointed.

> *Marianne is silent.*

ELINOR. Indeed!

> *Pause.*

ANNE. *(To Elinor.)* How do you like Devonshire, Miss Dashwood? I suppose you were very sorry to leave Sussex, and that big fine house—When your father died, and you lost all your money.

ELINOR. *(Taken aback.)* We were very sad to leave Norland.

MARIANNE. *(Mortally offended.)* Excuse me.

> *She goes to the piano and begins playing an angry march that continues, under.*

ANNE. *(Leaving no room for response.)* And had you a great many smart beaux there? There may be a vast many smart beaux in Exeter, I'm sure; but Lord knows if I can tell what beaux there might be about Norland! And perhaps the Miss Dashwoods might find it dull here if they do not have so many as they used to have. But perhaps you two do not care about the beaux, and had as lief be without! For my part, I think they are vastly agreeable provided they dress smart and behave civil. I can't bear to see them dirty and nasty. Now there's Mr. Rose at Exeter, clerk to Mr. Simpson, if you do but meet him of a morning he is not fit to be seen! I suppose your brother was quite a beau, Miss Dashwood, before he married, as he was so rich, and—

LUCY. —ANNE!

ANNE. *(Unchastened.)* Well. Sir John tells us Miss Marianne has a special admirer who is VERY handsome. And I hope you will have as good luck yourself soon—but perhaps you have a gentleman friend, already?

SIR JOHN. *(Shouting from offstage.)* His name is Ferrars, but pray do not tell it, for it's a great secret.

ANNE. Ferrars! Mr. Ferrars is the happy man? Your sister-in-law's brother, Miss Dashwood? Why, we know him very, very well.

LUCY. Anne! We have met Mr. Ferrars once or twice at our uncle's, but we hardly know him well.

ANNE. Well! I shall say no more, not for all the money in the world. I do believe I shall see if Miss Marianne knows any arias. I am passionately fond of an aria.

> *Anne sits and happily jabbers away at Marianne—Marianne inches as far away from her on the bench as possible, and plays even more angrily. Pause.*

LUCY. Miss Dashwood. Please pardon me, but I wonder if I might ask you something rather odd? Pray, are you closely acquainted with your sister-in-law's mother, Mrs. Ferrars?

ELINOR. No. I have never met her.

LUCY. Truly? Oh. I supposed she might have visited Norland sometimes.

ELINOR. No, I am afraid not.

LUCY. You must think me very strange for enquiring about her. I wish I could tell you why I ask; but I do not wish you to think me impertinent.

ELINOR. I—

LUCY. I could not bear to have you think me impertinent. I would rather anything in the world than be thought impertinent by a person like you.

ELINOR. I assure you—

LUCY. —And I do wish, so much, that I could tell you my reasons— and I would indeed be very glad of your advice in a trying matter. But I do not want to trouble you. I am sorry that you do not happen to know Mrs. Ferrars.

ELINOR. I am sorry that I do not. But I confess, I did not know that you were at all connected with that family.

LUCY. Forgive me, it was an odd question. Do not think of it any more.

> *Pause.*

ELINOR. Tea?

LUCY. Dearest Miss Dashwood, can I trust you?

ELINOR. Pardon?

LUCY. Can you—would you—keep a very great and grave and

important secret? If I unburdened myself to you entirely, would you solemnly promise never ever ever to tell anyone what I will tell you now?

Elinor nods, nonplussed.

Mrs. Ferrars is indeed nothing to me at present—but the time will come—when we may be very intimately connected indeed!

ELINOR. Good heavens! Have you an understanding with (*Lowering her voice.*) Mr. Robert Ferrars?

LUCY. No—I never saw him in my life; but I am engaged (*Fixing her eyes upon Elinor.*) to his eldest brother.

Pause.

I dare say he never dropped the smallest hint of it to you or your family? It is a great secret, for I have no fortune, and we fear his mother will take away all his inheritance if he chooses to marry a girl with no money.

ELINOR. I beg your pardon, but there must be some mistake. We cannot mean the same Mr. Edward Ferrars.

LUCY. I assure you, I am not mistaken about the name of the man on whom all my happiness depends. Mister. Edward. Ferrars.

The piano finishes in a huge, angry flourish as Elinor sits, alone.

End of Act One

ACT TWO

Edward's Engagement

The action picks back up from the end of Act One, as the piano music swells and then finishes in a great smash of angry chords. Elinor reacts.

ELINOR. Mr. Edward Ferrars.

LUCY. We can mean no other.

ELINOR. ...May I ask if your engagement is of long standing?

LUCY. We have been engaged these four years.

ELINOR. Four years!

Pause. In the background, Anne starts singing, badly.

LUCY. Yes. But we have known each other for far longer. He was a pupil for many years with my uncle, Mr. Pratt, who lives at Longstaple. He visited us there recently, in fact—oh! I suppose, just before he visited you here.

ELINOR. You are his friends in Plymouth?

LUCY. *I* am. Oh, no—did you think him sadly out of spirits? Poor Edward; it does break his heart terribly, for us to be separated. I gave him a lock of my hair set in a ring, and that was some comfort, he said, but not equal to us being together. Perhaps you noticed the ring when you saw him?

ANNE. Lucy! What is that song the doctor was asking me to sing last Thursday?

Lucy shoots her Death Eyes.

...Pardon my interruption.

She scurries back to the pianoforte.

LUCY. Miss Dashwood, I hope we can speak of this again. It is such a relief to confide in someone so much *older* and wiser! Until now, Anne is the only other person I have been able to ask advice of.

Looks at Anne pointedly.

And I know my dear Edward cannot be angry at me for confiding in you. He has told me so much about you and your family, and I know that he looks upon you quite as his own *sister.*

Anne warbles particularly badly.

Might we see you in London this winter?

ELINOR. No.

LUCY. I am sorry for that; we could have spent many happy hours together! Anne and I are going in December to see some relations— but I am really going to see my darling Edward. *(Leaning in, quietly.)* I will, of course, give him your very, very best.

She goes to her sister.

The Proposal

A week or two later. Elinor and Marianne visit at Barton Park. Marianne listlessly plays around on the piano, as:

MRS. JENNINGS. My dear Miss Dashwoods, gather 'round, gather 'round. Or, Miss Marianne, if you prefer, keep paddling away there, but do attend to me closely—I have a WONDERFUL proposal for you, my girls. Every winter, you know, I am in the habit of removing to a nice stomp in London, near Portman Square. But this year, I have been scheming, my little chickens, and I have hit upon it! I am entirely resolved that this go 'round, you both must come with me to town, as my guests, and keep a stupid old woman hopping!

ELINOR. *(Circumventing Marianne, who eagerly jumps up from the piano.)* I do thank you, ma'am; it is a very kind offer, but I'm afraid that we cannot leave my mother.

MRS. JENNINGS. Poo, I am sure she will not object! On the contrary, she will think me very fit to procure you both a bevy of eligible young London bachelors!

SIR JOHN. Miss Marianne seems eager enough! Our Mr. Willoughby lives in town, does he not?

MRS. JENNINGS. One or the other of you, I must have! I cannot live poking around by myself. Come, Miss Marianne, let us strike hands upon the bargain, and if Miss Elinor changes her mind by and by, why so much the better.

MARIANNE. I so sincerely thank you, ma'am. I must ask my mother's consent first, I suppose, but I assure you it would be almost the greatest happiness I could ever think of!

MRS. JENNINGS. *That* certainly sounds promising.

ELINOR. We will consult with Mamma, yes, but I think she will decide against it.

Marianne drags Elinor to Mrs. Dashwood.

Going to London

MRS. DASHWOOD. It is a wonderful plan!

MARGARET. Can't I go? *(Catching herself.)* May not I go?

MRS. DASHWOOD. Perhaps in a few years, my dear.

MARGARET. In a few years I will be beyond all improvement!

ELINOR. Mamma, I do not think this is prudent. Although Mrs. Jennings has a good heart, her protection cannot give us consequence in London— *(And.)*

MARIANNE. —If Elinor is frightened away by Mrs. Jennings, Mamma, it does not prevent MY accepting her invitation— *(And.)*

ELINOR. —what a sudden and miraculous display of enthusiasm for Mrs. Jennings!

MRS. DASHWOOD. I will have you BOTH go, these objections are nonsensical! You will enjoy touring London, and if Elinor would ever condescend to anticipate enjoyment, she might foresee having a very interesting time. John and Fanny always winter in town, and you shall have to visit them—and perhaps when doing so, you may encounter some *(Significantly.)* other members of the Ferrars family?

MARGARET. F-f-f-Ferrars—!

She is silenced by a Look from Elinor.

ELINOR. …I like Edward Ferrars well enough, but that is scarcely a reason to go all the way to London.

MARIANNE. Must you always be so cold?!

ELINOR. Marianne!

MARIANNE. Elinor, please! Just—don't you see that going to town may secure both of our happinesses, forever? *(Away from her mother.)* I cannot stand it, Elinor, I must see Willoughby or I will go mad. Please?

ELINOR. *(Pause.)* Please promise me that you'll behave yourself.

> *Marianne embraces her. The Gossips swoop in, pick them up, and transport them to London.*

London

> *They tumble out of the coach. Mrs. Jennings bustles off. Elinor stretches. Marianne hurries into their room, and immediately begins to write.*

ELINOR. Marianne, I am writing home tomorrow.

MARIANNE. I am not writing to my mother.

> *Marianne finishes the note with a large "W" and hands it to the Gossips, who snatch it eagerly, tearing it open and passing it along a line, reading and whispering as they sit. Marianne begins to pace. Elinor may begin to unpack. A day later. A servant enters. Marianne accosts him.*

Has any letter been delivered for me to-day?

SERVANT. No letter has been left but this.

MARIANNE. For me!

SERVANT. No, ma'am, for my mistress

> *He hurries away.*

ELINOR. You are expecting a letter, then?

MARIANNE. No.

ELINOR. You have no confidence in me, Marianne.

MARIANNE. Nay, Elinor, this reproach from YOU—you who confide in no one!

ELINOR. Me! Marianne, I again have nothing to tell.

MARIANNE. Nor I. Our situations are then alike. Neither of us has anything to tell; you, because you do not communicate, and I, because I conceal nothing.

> *Marianne continues to pace, in large circles. The Gossips may make tick-tock sounds.*

ELINOR. Marianne—

> *There is a rap on the door.*

MARIANNE. Elinor—it is him! Oh, oh—

> *She is almost ready to throw herself into Willoughby's arms, when Colonel Brandon appears.*

Oh.

> *It is too great a shock to be borne with calmness, and she immediately leaves the room.*

Colonel Brandon's Visit

Brandon tries to make the best of it.

COL. BRANDON. Miss Dashwood. I am pleased to see you in London.

MRS. JENNINGS. *(Bustling in, leaving no room for response.)* Oh! Colonel, I am monstrous glad to see you—beg your pardon, but I have been on my feet all day.

> *Collapses.*

I have brought two young ladies with me, you see—you see but one of them now, but there is another somewhere—and it is your friend, Miss Marianne! Yes! I thought that would please you. I do not know what you and Mr. Willoughby will do between you about her! It is a fine thing to be young and handsome—or so I think, I never was handsome, but I was young once, or so I seem to remember—Oh! Pardon me a moment, I have forgot to speak to Cook about dinner. One has always a world of little odd things to do after one has been away, and I have had old Cartwright to settle with—Lord, I have been as busy as a bee!

She bustles out again; as she does:

Buzz buzz buzz buzz!

COL. BRANDON. Miss Dashwood…might I congratulate you on the acquisition of a brother?

ELINOR. What do you mean?

COL. BRANDON. Your sister's engagement to Mr. Willoughby.

ELINOR. If she is engaged to Mr. Willoughby, this is the first time I have heard of it.

COL. BRANDON. Their marriage is universally talked of.

ELINOR. By whom?

COL. BRANDON. By some of whom you know nothing, by others with whom you are most intimate. *(In pain.)* Is it true, Miss Dashwood?

ELINOR. I…though they have never told me of their terms, of their mutual affection I have no doubt, and I am not surprised to hear of their engagement.

COL. BRANDON. To your sister I wish all imaginable happiness; to Willoughby, that he may endeavor to deserve her.

He bows and leaves.

MRS. JENNINGS. *(Reenters.)* Colonel, d'you prefer boiled fowls or veal cutlets? Colonel? Honestly, that man.

The Ball

Marianne reenters. They all prepare for the ball as Mrs. Jennings speaks.

MRS. JENNINGS. Three weeks gone by, and still no visit from Mr. Willoughby! It must be very teazing to you, Miss Marianne. But at the Fitzgeralds' ball, there will be many pretty fellows to attend upon you—and I'm sure Mr. Willoughby will turn up sharpish when he hears how many gentlemen you dance with tonight!

At the ball. It is crowded with people, some dancing, some chatting—a pressing crowd of Gossips. Music plays. Mrs.

Jennings is whisked away. Elinor and Marianne sit. Elinor sees Willoughby, at the other end of the room, in earnest conversation with a very well-dressed young woman. Elinor turns involuntarily to Marianne. At that moment Marianne sees him and, beaming, runs straight through the dancing couples to him, just stopping short. The music stops.

MARIANNE. Willoughby!!!

Elinor follows behind her, and tries to discreetly pull her back. Discomfited, Willoughby bows.

WILLOUGHBY. *(To Elinor.)* Miss Dashwood.

MARIANNE. Willoughby! Good God! Will you not shake hands with me?

He cannot avoid it, but holds her hand only for a moment.

WILLOUGHBY. *(Again to Elinor.)* I do hope that your mother is well.

MARIANNE. Have you not received my letters?

He does not respond.

For heaven's sake, Willoughby, what is the matter?

He looks at the woman standing next to him, who is watching with great interest.

WILLOUGHBY. I did receive the information about your arrival in town, which you were so good as to send me. Please excuse me.

He bows, lightly, and turns away. Marianne sways, fainting.

ELINOR. Marianne!

Elinor supports her, guiding her into a chair, trying to screen her from the observation of others. The Gossips surround her. Their dance becomes more and more predatory.

Pray, pray be composed, and do not betray what you feel to everybody present!

MARIANNE. Elinor! Go to him this moment, force him to come to me!

ELINOR. Marianne. No. With all of these people watching? Not now, dearest. Please.

MARIANNE. Oh, Elinor! I am unwell. I am very unwell.

The room resounds with whispers. The Gossip's dance may

become more and more vicious, until there is a climax of rumors, motion, and noise. Elinor, shielding Marianne, flees the scene.

The Morning After

The next morning, in the Dashwoods' room at Mrs. Jennings' London house. Marianne and Elinor are both asleep, still in their clothes. A knock on the door wakes them up.

MRS. JENNINGS. My dear Miss Marianne, I have something from a certain special someone, which I am sure you will find to your liking!

> *Marianne jumps up from the bed and flies to the door, grabbing the letter and running back to the bed. Elinor, just behind her, swiftly blocks the doorway.*

I never saw a young woman so desperately in love in my life! Pray, when are they to be married?

ELINOR. You don't really, Ma'am, believe that my sister is engaged to Mr. Willoughby! I always thought you were only joking.

MRS. JENNINGS. For shame, Miss Elinor! How can you talk so? We all know that they were madly in love with each other from the first moment they met! Because you are so sly about it personally, you think nobody else has any sense, but I tell you all society knows of it from here to Devonshire and back again. I tell everybody of it, myself!

ELINOR. Indeed, ma'am, you are mistaken. And you are doing a very unkind thing in spreading the report.

MRS. JENNINGS. Yes, yes. You are a very clever and subtle creature, Miss Elinor. Mum's the word until the banns are read, hey? *(Winking broadly.)* I am off to visit my Charlotte, but have asked Susan to lay out a nice breakfast for you two to stuff yourselves! Ta-ta!

> *Elinor rushes back into the bedroom, where Marianne sits, holding the letter. She reads the letter out loud.*

ELINOR. "My dear madam, I gather that something in my behavior last night did not meet with your approval, although I am at a loss as to how I offended you. Allow me to be plain: I am sorry if you ever mistook my friendship for something more, but you must acknowledge that anything of that nature is and has been impossible—as my affections have long been engaged with another young lady. John Willoughby."

MARIANNE. Elinor, what shall I do? What shall I do? *(Getting hysterical.)*

ELINOR. Marianne, please! Try to stay calm!

MARIANNE. How can I be calm?!!

ELINOR. What good does it do to become hysterical?!

MARIANNE. Leave me if it upsets you so much!

ELINOR. Do not indulge in this display!

MARIANNE. Leave me, hate me, forget me! But do not ask me not to feel!

ELINOR. Marianne, it might have been worse! Your engagement could have gone on much longer before he ended it!

MARIANNE. What engagement?

ELINOR. You weren't engaged?! But Marianne, you *wrote* to him!

MARIANNE. Leave me alone, leave me alone!

> *She sobs. Mrs. Jennings, without knocking, hurries in. The Gossips crowd outside the door.*

MRS. JENNINGS. How do you do, my dear?

> *Marianne howls.*

Poor thing, she looks very bad.—And no wonder, it is but too true. He is to be married very soon. Mrs. Taylor told me of it downstairs, and I almost sank on the spot! Well, said I, if this is true, he has used a young lady of my acquaintance abominably ill, and I wish with all my soul his wife may plague his heart out. But he is not the only man in the world worth having, Miss Marianne! You will soon be beating them back with a stout stick!

> *Marianne half-screams.*

Yes, have your little cry out. *(Moving away from the bed; to Elinor, in a not-quiet stage whisper.)* Luckily, the Parrys and Sandersons are coming tonight, and that will amuse her!

ELINOR. *(Attempts to usher her out of the room.)* Dear ma'am, I am sure Marianne will not leave her room today.

MRS. JENNINGS. I cannot believe that a man should use a pretty girl so ill! But when there is plenty of money on one side, and none on the other…

ELINOR. The lady then—is very rich?

MRS. JENNINGS. Fifty thousand pounds, my dear. The young Miss Grey—a stylish girl they say, but not handsome. Fifty thousand pounds! And it won't come before it's wanted, for they say he is all to pieces! Well, 'tis a true saying about an ill-wind, for it will be all the better for Colonel Brandon! How he'll chuckle over this news! They'll be married by Mid-summer. I shall spirit him up as soon as I can—maybe he'll come tonight. One shoulder of mutton, you know, drives another down!

> *She scampers off. Elinor turns back into the room and approaches the bed.*

MARIANNE. All she wants is gossip, and she only likes me because I supply her with it.

ELINOR. Marianne.

MARIANNE. I do not want to talk.

ELINOR. I will leave you, if you will promise to rest.

> *Marianne pulls the covers over her head. Mrs. Jennings knocks at the door.*

MRS. JENNINGS. I recollected that I had some fine old Constantia wine in the house, so I have brought a glass of it for your sister. My poor husband was very fond of it whenever he had a touch of his gout.

ELINOR. How good you are, ma'am.

> *Mrs. Jennings slips off. Elinor looks at Marianne, who is still under the covers, and tosses off the wine herself.*

Colonel Brandon's Revelation

The next morning. Elinor sits and attempts to compose herself in the drawing room. She begins to write to her mother.

SERVANT. Colonel Brandon, miss.

Elinor hurriedly hides the letter and smooths her hair. Colonel Brandon enters.

ELINOR. I am afraid Mrs. Jennings is away from home, Colonel.

COL. BRANDON. And your sister?

ELINOR. Marianne is...unwell.

COL. BRANDON. Perhaps, then, what I heard this morning—there may be more truth in it than I thought possible.

ELINOR. What did you hear?

COL. BRANDON. It concerned a certain gentleman.

ELINOR. You mean Mr. Willoughby's sudden engagement to Miss Grey. Have you also heard that Miss Grey has fifty thousand pounds?

COL. BRANDON. ...How is your sister?

ELINOR. Her sufferings have been very severe.

COL. BRANDON. Miss Dashwood, I may be able to offer some comfort—no, not comfort, but I may be able to relate some—history about Mr. Willoughby which may bring some...clarity.

ELINOR. Please go on.

COL. BRANDON. You may find me a very awkward narrator.

ELINOR. Please.

COL. BRANDON. In my youth, I knew a lady who...was very like your sister Marianne, both in person and in temperament. I loved her, and she loved me in return—but Eliza had no fortune, and I was a young man with no independence and no occupation. I was under my father's power.

Beat.

He forbade the match, of course. A marriage of that kind was impossible, he said, unthinkable—and though I protested violently, I am ashamed to say that he won his point at the last. Threatened with disinheritance and disownment, I faltered. And Eliza was sent away.

Pause.

At seventeen, I was also shipped off to my regiment in the East Indies, and there lost contact with Eliza entirely. A man came along, and treated her kindly for a time…and then another, and then another. I returned to England a grown man, independent—and determined to find her. By the time I did, she was dying in the poorhouse, her infant by her side. You may have heard some rumors about my ward, Miss Jane Williams. She is Eliza's daughter, whom I swore to look after as my own. That was fifteen years ago. Last February, Jane suddenly disappeared from her boarding school; for months, I could not find her. Finally, I received a letter from her—on that evening I left Barton so suddenly. In it, she did not name the man who had seduced her—his luck, for I would have done him violence at the table, even as he basked in your sister's smiles.

ELINOR. Mr. Willoughby.

COL. BRANDON. He left Jane in a situation of the utmost distress, with no home, no help, no friends, ignorant of his whereabouts. She is fifteen. And now she is with child.

ELINOR. This is beyond everything!

COL. BRANDON. When I came to you last week, I thought that all was settled between your sister and Mr. Willoughby. I did not know how I could stop the marriage without heaping scandal upon both her and my poor Jane.

ELINOR. Who knows what his designs on Marianne were!

COL. BRANDON. I promise you, Miss Dashwood, if I did not from my heart believe that this might eventually lessen Miss Marianne's regrets, I would never have burdened you with such troubling information.

He bows.

I am sure I keep you from your sister.

He leaves. Elinor, with a heavy heart, goes up to the bedroom.

ELINOR. Marianne, before I write to Mamma—I have something I need to tell you…

She continues under the Gossips, who chatter:

The Gossips Take Measure

GOSSIP 3. I suppose you heard about Mr. Willoughby's very... expeditious nuptials?

GOSSIP 5. I heard that his creditors breathe much easier!

GOSSIP 4. I heard that Miss Grey wore orange blossoms to their wedding...orange blossoms! At this time of year!

GOSSIP 3. They say the younger Miss Dashwood is broken-hearted, and very ill—they had been *corresponding*, you know.

GOSSIP 5. Indeed!

GOSSIP 3. Oh yes, she wrote to him openly!

GOSSIP 4. Very forward of her!

GOSSIP 5. No one to keep her in check?

GOSSIP 1. The father is dead, you know.

GOSSIP 3. Well, what can you expect—

GOSSIP 1. —I heard that she went out riding with him, alone.

GOSSIP 4. —I am not surprised!

GOSSIP 2. —I am sure all of the Dashwood girls run quite wild—

GOSSIP 1. —And no money at all to speak of—

GOSSIP 2. —Then what did she expect?

GOSSIP 4. Poor girl!

GOSSIP 3. Silly girl!

GOSSIP 1. Very forward!

GOSSIP 5. Very foolish!

GOSSIP 3. What a waste!

After the Scandal

Marianne sits on her bed, staring into space. Elinor sits with her.

ELINOR. And so you see that we never really knew Willoughby at all.

    Pause.

…Marianne?

MARIANNE. I would sooner think myself deceived by all the world than by Willoughby.

ELINOR. He has practiced nothing but deceit, from beginning to end!

MARIANNE. I cannot explain his behavior towards that poor girl, but whatever his sins, I know that he loved me. He loves me. That much is true.

ELINOR. Did he tell you that he loved you?

MARIANNE. Yes—no. Never absolutely. It does not matter.

ELINOR. Of course it does. He is the worst kind of villain.

MARIANNE. No, he isn't! Not at heart. You say that we never knew him, Elinor, but I did, I knew him as I know myself! If he is wicked, then perhaps so am I. He and I are the same.

ELINOR. You are not being reasonable!

MARIANNE. You do not understand.

ELINOR. Perhaps I don't! Marianne, how could you have written to him?

MARIANNE. I felt myself to be as solemnly engaged to him, as if the strictest legal covenant had bound us!

ELINOR. Obviously, he did not feel the same.

MARIANNE. He DID! Elinor, I may have been cruelly used; but not by Willoughby.

ELINOR. Who else but Willoughby?

MARIANNE. I do not know!

ELINOR. Well, whoever may have been your enemy, let them be cheated of their triumph, by seeing you rise above these circumstances!

MARIANNE. I care not who knows that I am wretched! It is easy for those who have no sorrow to talk of calmness and exertion!

ELINOR. Do you think I have no sorrow, Marianne? *(Restraining herself.)* ...Can you believe me capable of being at ease, when I see you in this state?

MARIANNE. Forgive me: I know that you feel for me, and I am very sorry to make you unhappy. But mine is a misery which nothing can ever do away.

> *Beat.*

I want to go home.

John Calls

> *John Dashwood sails in, surrounded by several Gossips. They prepare him for the party as he speaks, as much to them as to Elinor and Marianne. He is part of the machine.*

JOHN. My dear sisters! So delightful to see you in town! Fanny and I wanted to stop in on you earlier, of course, but you know we have been very busy visiting and being visited!

GOSSIP 1. Visit!

GOSSIP 4. Visit!

GOSSIP 3. Visit visit visit!

MARIANNE. Pardon me.

> *She sits.*

JOHN. Whatever is the matter with Marianne? She looks very unwell.

ELINOR. She has had a nervous complaint.

JOHN. Oh, I am sorry for that. At her time of life, anything of an illness destroys the bloom forever!

GOSSIP 1. Too pale!

GOSSIP 4. Too thin!

GOSSIP 3. Too pale and thin!

GOSSIP 2. (She's not that thin.)

JOHN. Fanny used to say that Marianne would certainly marry better than you did, but the way she looks NOW, I doubt she will catch a man worth more than five or six hundred a year.

The Gossips all cock their heads, assessing Marianne, and then go about their business.

You will excuse me, twittering about marriage like an old dowager—but we have all been talking of nothing else in my household! It is finally time, you know, for Edward to settle.

ELINOR. Is Mr. Ferrars going to be married?

JOHN. It is not battened down entirely—yet—but his mother has determined she will give him his independence just as soon as he marries the honorable Miss Morton.

GOSSIP 1. Lord Morton's daughter!

GOSSIP 4. She comes with thirty thousand pounds!

GOSSIP 3. THIRTY THOUSAND POUNDS!

ELINOR. And what does Mr. Ferrars think of the arrangement?

JOHN. I do not know if his mother has told him yet. No doubt he will be delighted! It is an excellent match! But that's all to come—in the meantime, we wanted to invite you to a little dinner party. You must attend—Fanny is wild to see you!

GOSSIP 1. A party!

GOSSIP 4. A party!

GOSSIP 3. A party, party, party!!

The Party

The Gossips move them all into the party. The most powerful figure in the room is Mrs. Ferrars, Edward and Fanny's mother, a wisened, unpleasant old woman—she may even be represented by a nasty puppet on Fanny's hand. Robert Ferrars, Edward's younger brother and a complete twit, stands with Fanny and his mother. Marianne and Elinor walk in to find a most unpleasant surprise—the Miss Steeles.

ELINOR. Miss Steele!

LUCY. Miss Dashwood. Miss Marianne.

ANNE. Oh, look, Lucy! It's our particular friends!

ELINOR. ...How do you happen to be in this company?

LUCY. I may as well ask the same thing of you—I confess that I am amazed to see you! For you TOLD me, you know, that you would not ever come to town at all—and yet here you are.

MARIANNE. *(At the end of her rope.)* Why are you here?

ANNE. Why, we two and your sister-in-law are the fastest of friends! Yes! Isn't that funny? Last week, we were in the sweetest little milliner's shop, on Bradley Street, and we fell to talking with a terribly elegant lady waiting there, and chatting about her boy, who was being quite a monkey with the hats—I thought the milliner should faint—and Lucy has such a way with children, and one thing led to another, and it turned out that elegant lady was Mrs. John Dashwood, and we have visited almost every day since then, and she invited us to the party, and look, HERE WE ARE.

> *Beat.*

...Now isn't that funny?!

JOHN. *(Approaching.)* Oh, good! You have all discovered each other, I see—what a small world, that you were all such friends already! Come, ladies—let me introduce you.

LUCY. Miss Dashwood! *(Turning to Elinor and squeezing her hand.)* Pray for me! In a moment I shall meet the person that is to be my mother!

JOHN. Our host, Mrs. Ferrars.

> *All bow or curtsy as appropriate. Mrs. Ferrars very pointedly turns away from Elinor and mumbles to John.*

Yes, ma'am. Mrs. Ferrars says that the Miss Steeles are exceedingly pretty.

> *Polite murmur. They all sit down, uncomfortably. Conversation starts up. Robert Ferrars strolls up to Elinor and makes a flourishing little bow.*

ROBERT FERRARS. Miss Dashwood. Robert Ferrars. You reside in Devonshire, I am told—in a cottage.

ELINOR. We do.

ROBERT FERRARS. For my own part, I am excessively fond of a cottage; there is always so much elegance in a cottage. If I had any money to spare, I should build a cottage, and have all my friends visit me. In my cottage. I advise everybody I see to build a cottage. My intimate friend Lord Courtland—of the Lancashire Courtlands—came to me the other day, and laid before me three different architectural schemes. "Which one should I build, Robby?" said he. "My dear Courtland," said I, throwing them all directly into the fire, "do not build any of these deplorable shacks, but by all means build a cottage." A cottage, man. A cottage, a cottage, a cottage! And THAT was the end of THAT.

ELINOR. *(Pause.)* Indeed.

> *He bows again.*

ROBERT FERRARS. *(Turning to Lucy Steele.)* And you, Miss Steele. Do you live in a cottage?

LUCY. I do not.

ROBERT FERRARS. *(Eyeing her.)* More's the pity.

> *He saunters away.*

LUCY. *(Watching him walk away; to Elinor.)* And that is Edward's brother! They are…very unlike. *(Recalling herself.)* Mrs. Dashwood, I cannot thank you enough for your invitation to dine tonight. Anne and I are quite overwhelmed by your generosity! I only hope we do not intrude!

FANNY. Oh, Miss Lucy. How could a charming creature such as

you ever intrude?

Mrs. Ferrars whispers in her ear, eying Elinor.

Indeed, Mother—Mother says how unusual it is, nowadays, to encounter young women who are as modest and respectful as *les jolies* Miss Steeles. I assure you, my dear—young ladies of *your* sort are always welcome here.

LUCY. Oh, Mrs. Ferrars, you are too kind. I could just stay here forever! *(Doing a truly elaborate curtsy. Anne imitates it badly.)* Your home is so lovely! These sketches on the wall—so well-executed! Did you draw them, Mrs. Dashwood?

JOHN. These were done by Elinor.

Lucy could shoot herself for the error. He takes the sketches down and shows them to her.

FANNY. Do you know, we should ask Miss Morton to paint something for us. She DOES paint most delightfully!

JOHN. Beautifully indeed! But SHE does everything well.

MARIANNE. Who is Miss Morton? Why are you talking about Miss Morton?—Elinor made these, and they are beautiful.

She snatches the sketches from John's hand.

MRS. FERRARS. Miss Morton is LORD MORTON'S DAUGHTER.

There is a tense silence.

MARIANNE. Dear, dear Elinor, don't mind them. Please don't let them make YOU unhappy.

She bursts into tears, still holding the sketches, burying her head in Elinor's lap. Fanny stands, fairly pleased by the whole exchange.

FANNY. Shall we go in for dinner?

The rest file in for dinner.

Lucy's Visit

The next day; Lucy sails in and sits next to Elinor, in Mrs. Jennings' parlor.

LUCY. My dearest, dearest friend! Can you believe it?

ELINOR. What, exactly?

LUCY. Did you not see Mrs. Ferrars' way of treating me yesterday? So exceedingly affable! So kind, from the moment I was introduced! She really seemed to take a special fancy to me! Were you not quite struck with it?!

ELINOR. She was certainly very civil to you.

LUCY. Did you see nothing but civility?

ELINOR. If his family knew about your engagement, nothing could be more promising than their treatment of you. But as that is not the case—

LUCY. Why in the world would they pretend to like me, if they did not? Mrs. Ferrars is affability itself, and so is your sister-in-law, and I think it will all work out SPLENDIDLY, and all my fears were for nothing!

> *Pause.*

ELINOR. I suppose time will tell.

> *Pause.*

LUCY. Why did you never mention, Miss Dashwood, how exceedingly charming your sister-in-law is? She is generosity itself. She wrote Anne and I a little note this morning and invited both of us to stay with her for a bit; isn't that very delightful?

> *Beat.*

Are you ill, Miss Dashwood?—You seem rather low.

ELINOR. I never was in better health.

LUCY. Really? You do not look it. Oh, I am so glad that his mother loves me already! I would have given up all hope if she had treated me in a forbidding sort of way, and made clear that I was unwelcome! For when she DOES dislike people, I know it is most unshakable and violent!

The door is thrown open.

SERVANT. Mr. Edward Ferrars, Miss.

> *Edward walks in. It is impossibly awkward. Edward starts violently and almost walks right back out.*

ELINOR. Mr. Ferrars!

EDWARD. Miss Dashwood. Miss…Steele.

> *He lurches unsteadily towards the chair. He manages to knock a book off the table, grabs it, and puts it on the table again. He then bobs to sit, then stands.*

ELINOR. Please, do be seated.

EDWARD. I…thank you. Miss Dashwood.

> *He covers the ring on his hand, then uncovers it under Lucy's sharp eyes.*

I came to…enquire after your mother.

ELINOR. She is very well, thank you.

EDWARD. Excellent. And young Miss Margaret? *(Unnecessarily.)* …Your sister?

ELINOR. Very well. Very well, thank you!

> *Marianne rushes in, holding out her hand to be shaken, with great relief and joy.*

MARIANNE. Edward! I heard you announced.

EDWARD. Miss Marianne. How do you do?

MARIANNE. Oh, I am very unwell. But don't think of me, Edward! Elinor is well, you see. And surely that is all that matters.

EDWARD. Does not… *(Tripping over his words.)* does not London not agree with you?

MARIANNE. Not at all. I expected to find much pleasure here, but…the sight of you is the only comfort it has afforded thus far.

EDWARD. *(Half-listening to her.)* Ah.

MARIANNE. *(Pause.)* We spent such a terrible, wretched day at Harley Street yesterday, Edward! I have so much to say to you about it, *(Looking at Lucy.)* which cannot be said at the moment. But why weren't you there?

EDWARD. I am afraid I was engaged elsewhere.

MARIANNE. Engaged elsewhere?! When such friends were to be met?

LUCY. Perhaps, Miss Marianne, you think that young men never keep any engagements at all!

Elinor is very angry, but the sting goes right over Marianne's head.

MARIANNE. Not so, indeed; I am sure he must have had something very important to do, to keep him from us. Did you have some pressing previous obligation, Edward?

Edward chokes on some tea—vaguely nods.

I knew it! What else could have kept you away? Edward really has the most active conscience in the whole world, you know, and would only have disappointed us because he did not want to break his word to another. Indeed, he is the most fearful of failing expectations, or causing pain to others of anybody I ever met, and he always tries to do the right thing—whether it makes him happy or not! Edward, it is so, and I will say it!

The nature of her commendation is very un-exhilarating to Edward.

EDWARD. Please do excuse me, I have only come for a moment, I have an appointment to see a horse. To buy. I may buy the horse. If it is a good horse.

MARIANNE. Going so soon! Again! Edward, this must not be.

LUCY. I am afraid I must also be on my way. If you are leaving, Mr. Ferrars, perhaps you would be so good as to escort me as far as the park?

EDWARD. I…why, yes. Delighted. Miss Marianne. Miss Dashwood.

Lucy sweeps a curtsy. They exit.

MARIANNE. What could have brought her here? Could she not see that we wanted her gone!—How teazing to Edward!

ELINOR. Why so?—We are all his friends, and he has known Lucy the longest. I am sure that he was happy to see her.

MARIANNE. *(Looking at her steadily.)* You know, Elinor—I cannot bear when you say things that you know are not true.

The News

The next day. Mrs. Jennings rushes in, in a state of absolutely breathless excitement.

MRS. JENNINGS. Miss Dashwood! Miss Marianne! Have you heard the news? At your sister's house! A scandal! *(With great enthusiasm.)* A real scandal!

> *Fanny sits, doing needlework. Anne sits with her, desultorily doing the same.*

ANNE. I cannot think what is taking Lucy so long at her toilette this morning. She must fix a ribbon in her hair, too, I suppose, after seeing mine. *(Patting her own hair.)*

FANNY. *Cette ribbon* suits you marvelously, my dear. *Très jolie. (Off of Anne's look of complete incomprehension.)* Very pretty.

ANNE. Oh, now, YOU are going to laugh at me, too. But why shouldn't I wear pink ribbons? Pink is the doctor's favorite color, true, but that doesn't mean that I wear it just to please him!

FANNY. You young ladies and your beaux! It is all so diverting.

ANNE. *(Simpering.)* Oh, la.

FANNY. But you must not keep every heart for yourself, Miss Anne! You must leave some suitors for dear Miss Lucy.

ANNE. Oh, Lucy gets more than enough attention, ma'am.

FANNY. Pray tell!

ANNE. Lucy has a beau herself, though not a soul knows of it but me. I have a vast deal I could say to you on that account, were I so free.

FANNY. Now, Miss Anne! You know Miss Lucy and yourself are family to me—and I am afraid that we permit no secrets in this family. I will ask you again, Madame—who is the lucky gentleman, and where is his lodging?

ANNE. Oh no, I mustn't tell, ma'am. *(Desperately attempting to change the subject.)* My, if you aren't wearing that new spotted muslin…

FANNY. No, no… I shall not be put off so easily!

ANNE. Lord! Well…you are so fond of Lucy, I'm sure there will be

73

no difficulty. But you musn't tell her that I told you! She is engaged, ma'am!

LUCY. *(From offstage.)* Anne!

FANNY. Engaged!

ANNE. To—

> *Anne whispers it in her ear. Fanny looks at her and starts screaming hysterically. She throws the needlework at Anne. Anne begins to scream. Lucy runs in; Fanny lunges toward her. Lucy starts screaming. John Dashwood runs in and restrains Fanny, as does a maid. Lucy slaps Anne. Hysteria. Lucy faints. Anne is crawling about on her knees, crying, etc.*

MRS. JENNINGS. Your sister-in-law threw them out of the house and fell into fits, and your brother was so frightened that he sent for Dr. Donavan, and Dr. Donavan found the house in an uproar, and now the story is ALL OVER TOWN. Myself, I had no notion of people's making such a to-do about money and greatness!

> *The Gossips flee to spread the word, cackling amongst themselves. Marianne sinks down.*

Miss Marianne! Are you ill?

ELINOR. I think my sister wants rest, Mrs. Jennings. Please let me attend to her.

> *She ushers her into their room and shuts the door.*

Edward Is to Be Married

ELINOR. Marianne—I knew.

MARIANNE. Has Edward written to you?

ELINOR. I have known it these four months. Lucy told it to me herself, and swore me to secrecy before I knew what I was promising.

MARIANNE. How have you borne it?

ELINOR. What else was there to do?

MARIANNE. For four months!—And yet you do love him?

ELINOR. Yes. But I do not love only him—and I was glad to spare my loved ones from my unhappiness.

MARIANNE. How could Edward be engaged to that creature?

ELINOR. People make mistakes, Marianne. He was very young when he met Lucy, and confined as he was by his mother and upbringing, I am sure that she was very...refreshing. She is lively, and can make herself agreeable, when she wishes. And if, when he grew older, he perhaps began to see something of her true nature, I am sure that he was too honorable to break off the engagement. Edward, as we have always said, has a most active conscience.

MARIANNE. But his behavior towards you!

ELINOR. I must acquit Edward of all essential misconduct.

MARIANNE. Elinor!

ELINOR. He never promised me anything, Marianne. It's not his fault that we got carried away by our own conjectures.

MARIANNE. I am sure that he feels something for you.

ELINOR. Even if that is true, there is nothing to be done about it. Edward will marry Lucy. And I truly wish him very happy.

MARIANNE. If your way of thinking is so...practical, I am not surprised that you are calm.

ELINOR. *(It is deeply painful.)* I understand. You do not suppose that I have ever felt much. For four months, Marianne, I have known of Edward's engagement. For four months, I have had to listen to Lucy's hopes and exultations again and again. For four months, I have never been able to confide in anyone. I am to be divided from Edward forever. Nothing has ever proved him unworthy, and I believe now that perhaps he does—feel something, as you say. In short, I have suffered all of the punishments of extreme attachment, without enjoying any of its advantages. If you think me capable of ever feeling anything, Marianne, surely you can imagine that I have felt this loss very deeply. My current composure is the product of my constant and painful exertion to maintain control over myself. I have done my duty. But believe me—I have been VERY unhappy.

MARIANNE. Elinor—I do not know what to say.

ELINOR. Promise me something, Marianne.

MARIANNE. Anything!

ELINOR. Promise never to speak about the matter with the least appearance of bitterness. Speak civilly and discreetly about it to every-one who may enquire—Yes, even Edward and Lucy.

MARIANNE. But—

ELINOR. Please.

MARIANNE. Yes, yes! Of course. I promise.

John Relates the News

A crowd of Gossips gathers around. John Dashwood addresses Elinor, Marianne, and Mrs. Jennings, as well as the Gossips. Marianne tries very hard not to speak her mind.

JOHN. You have heard, I suppose, of the very shocking discovery that took place under our roof yesterday.

GOSSIP 1. Shocking!

GOSSIP 4. Appalling!

GOSSIP 3. Absurd!

JOHN. Fanny says she shall never think well of anybody again, after being so deceived!—"I now wish," said poor Fanny, "that we had even asked your sisters to stay with us, instead of the Steeles."

ELINOR. Why, thank you.

GOSSIP 1. Generous!

GOSSIP 4. Most generous!

MARIANNE. Mmm!

JOHN. We sent for Edward. But I am sorry to relate what happened. His mother explained that she would give him his independence if he would simply give up the girl and marry Miss Morton; told him even that she would settle on him the Norfolk estate, which brings in a good thousand a year. But if he chose to marry Miss Steele, she would disown him entirely, and indeed, if he tried to find any profession at all, she would do everything she could to prevent him from advancing in it.

MARIANNE. *(Indignantly.)* Gracious God!

JOHN. Well may you exclaim, Marianne, at Mrs. Ferrars' generosity!

Marianne is going to retort, but looks at Elinor, and only changes seats.

Edward said very little, but what he did say was unfeeling indeed to his mother and sister, who strove with all their might to help him see the error of his ways. He refused to give up his engagement. He will stand to it, though it ruins him.

MRS. JENNINGS. Then he has acted like an honest man! I beg your pardon, Mr. Dashwood, but I have some concern in the business, for Lucy Steele is my relation!

JOHN. I do not mean to speak disrespectfully of any connection of yours, Madam, but in the present case you know, the match is impossible.

MRS. JENNINGS. Well, sir, and how did it end?

GOSSIP 4. What is to happen?

GOSSIP 3. Did his mother cast him off?

GOSSIP 4. Is he ruined entirely?

JOHN. I am sorry to say, ma'am, it finished in a most unhappy rupture. Edward is dismissed forever from Mrs. Ferrars' notice, and will be disinherited. His mother has determined, with a very natural kind of spirit, to give it all to Robert immediately.

GOSSIP 3. Thus ends Edward Ferrars, the great untrappable rich bachelor!

GOSSIP 4. How does he propose to marry ANYONE now that he's penniless?

GOSSIP 3. Impossible!

GOSSIP 1. And Mr. Robert Ferrars is a rich man!

GOSSIP 4. A very rich man!

GOSSIP 3. And very unmarried…

The Gossips eye each other, then scramble off to get Robert Ferrars in their clutches.

JOHN. It is indeed a grave situation. I see the natural anxiety upon your faces, but do not worry—there is no material danger to Fanny's health, although she suffers severely, the angel!

He takes his leave.

Leaving London

MRS. JENNINGS. This town gets worse every year, my dears—bad behavior all around. Thank heavens that we'll be back in Barton soon! We will stop only for a visit with my daughter Charlotte at Cleveland, and then we'll be home again, as quick as you please!

MARIANNE. Cleveland! No, I cannot go to Cleveland!

MRS. JENNINGS. Oh! Because Mr. Willoughby has property in the county? Indeed, they are almost neighbors—I think one can see his home from a hill on Charlotte's estate. Oh, I am sorry! But you will never see him, my dear. I have told Charlotte all about his wicked treatment of you, and her dear Mr. Palmer would shoot him like a pheasant on sight! You will be very safe, I assure you.

ELINOR. Ma'am, thank you. We are very happy to go with you—it is an excellent plan. *(Hurrying Marianne away.)*

MARIANNE. Elinor, you cannot expect me to go.

ELINOR. Marianne, we will only be there a few days, and we shall remain in the house the entire time. I promise you, there is no chance that you will see him! We may even ask Colonel Brandon to escort us back home from there. Please. It is the quickest, most eligible manner in which to return, and you know we are both eager to be gone.

Colonel Brandon's Proposition

COL. BRANDON. I would be honored to escort you whenever you wish to leave the Palmers'.

Elinor presses his hand gratefully.

Miss Dashwood—I must speak to you about another matter. I have heard of the injustice your friend Mr. Ferrars has suffered, and I wondered if I might be of some use.

ELINOR. How so?

COL. BRANDON. They say that Mr. Ferrars intends to enter the church. The living of Delaford is vacant, and mine to appoint. Would you be willing to tell him that I would name him as rector, if he thinks it worth his acceptance? I only wish it were more valuable, but it is enough for him to marry upon.

ELINOR. That is very generous, Colonel. But wouldn't you rather offer him the position yourself?

COL. BRANDON. I do not know him well, Miss Dashwood; I have only met him two or three times. I should think, as you are his old friend, he would be more inclined to hear the happy news from you.

Elinor, trapped, inclines her head.

Edward and Elinor Meet

EDWARD. Miss Dashwood. I received a note from Mrs. Jennings. That—that you wished to speak with me?

ELINOR. Yes! Hello. Yes. I have something of consequence to inform you of. I am charged with a most agreeable office! *(Trying to make the best of it and having some difficulty.)* Our dear friend, Colonel Brandon, has desired me to say, that understanding you mean to take orders, he has great pleasure in offering you the living of Delaford. Allow me to congratulate you, and to join in his wish that it may allow you to—establish all your views of *(Looking for the correct word.)* domesticity. *(Regrets using that word.)*

EDWARD. Colonel Brandon?

ELINOR. Yes. Colonel Brandon has heard of your troubles and wishes to help in any way that he can. As do we all.

EDWARD. Colonel Brandon give me a living!—

ELINOR. The unkindness of your family has made you astonished to find kindness anywhere.

EDWARD. No.

He regards her seriously.

I am sure I owe this to you.

ELINOR. You are very much mistaken. I have had no hand in it. Not that I wouldn't have. Had a hand in it. If I had had a hand to give in it.

Awkward pause.

EDWARD. Miss Dashwood. When I became engaged to Miss Steele, I was very young, and quite…stupid, really.

Another awkward pause.

Colonel Brandon lodges, I think, on St. James Street.

ELINOR. I believe so.

EDWARD. I must hurry away then, to thank him.

ELINOR. May…may I give you my unceasing good wishes for your happiness.

EDWARD. And mine for yours.

Pause.

Miss Dashwood.

He bows and leaves. As Elinor broods, the Gossips sweep her, Marianne, and Mrs. Jennings up and take them to Cleveland. Marianne and Elinor both look rather the worse for wear.

Cleveland

MRS. JENNINGS. And here we are! Miss Elinor, Miss Marianne, Colonel, may I introduce Charlotte, the prettiest of my daughters? Ooh, Charlotte, you have grown so plump!

She exits. Colonel Brandon exits with her, leaving the sisters alone for a moment.

MARIANNE. I am so stiff from the carriage. I may take a little walk around the grounds.

ELINOR. It is so late, and looks as if it may rain—wait only until tomorrow, and I will walk with you.

MARIANNE. It is not going to rain! I shall go mad if I do not walk, Elinor. I will return soon.

ELINOR. At least take your shawl!

Marianne has already moved away. It, naturally, begins to rain. Marianne doesn't feel it at all; she continues to walk, steadily, her eyes on the hill. The Gossips surround her and pull her, part of the storm. They whisper maliciously about her, buffeting her. She reaches the summit fighting them, and stares at what she imagines must be the edge of Willoughby's property.

MARIANNE. Willoughby!

The Gossips lift and take her, as if taking her away to be sacrificed. She is seized by violent chills and coughing as they transport her to a bed. They strip her as she crawls into bed, only in a shift. Elinor enters and sits by her side, feeling her forehead. The Gossips chatter as they tuck her in.

GOSSIP 4. A bilious complaint?

GOSSIP 1. No! A fever, they say, and very serious.

GOSSIP 2. Her father died from the same, you know!

GOSSIP 3. That stock was never strong.

GOSSIP 4. Dying of a broken heart!

GOSSIP 2. Such a rapid decay!

GOSSIP 1. They say the doctor has been there four times in two days, and the Palmers have removed themselves, lest it be contagious.

GOSSIP 4. Molly has from Cook that the doctor is very grave, and grows graver still.

GOSSIP 1. Well, that's the sad end of the whole affair, I suppose. And her so young!

They gather around Marianne just as they gathered around her father's corpse.

GOSSIP 5. Poor Miss Dashwood.

GOSSIP 3. Poor Miss Dashwood.

GOSSIP 4. Poor Miss Dashwood.

GOSSIP 1. Poor Miss Dashwood.

They shrug their shoulders and leave.

Very Serious

Marianne lies in bed. The doctor examines her as Elinor hovers.

MARIANNE. *(Starting violently.)* Elinor! Is Mamma coming?—

ELINOR. Not yet, *(With an attempt at cheerfulness.)* we will send for her, but it may take some time for her to get here.

MARIANNE. But she must not go by London! I shall never see her, if she goes by London.

ELINOR. Marianne?

MARIANNE. *(In confusion.)* Elinor, please… I am hot. I am too hot!

ELINOR. Doctor, she is not herself…

DOCTOR. *(Taking her pulse.)* I will bleed her.

ELINOR. I shall hold the bowl.

DOCTOR. Miss Dashwood

He takes the bowl from her.

—I would prefer if you would send a man in. I cannot have you fainting.

Elinor turns to leave.

Miss Dashwood, it might be best if your mother was sent for. Soon.

Elinor leaves the sickroom and sits for a moment, trembling, trying to soothe herself. Colonel Brandon is pacing in the same room—he goes to her, but she holds up a hand to ward him off. They hear Marianne being bled from the other room.

MARIANNE. *(Like a child.)* Ow! Ow…

COL. BRANDON. Is she going to die?

ELINOR. I must dispatch a messenger to Barton for my mother. She must come as soon as possible.

COL. BRANDON. *(Understands.)* With your leave, I will bring the message myself; it will be faster, and I will bring her back with me directly.

ELINOR. That is not necessary, Colonel.

COL. BRANDON. Miss Dashwood. Give me something to do. I will return with your mother—look for us before ten o'clock.

She nods her head. He quickly presses her hand and leaves. Elinor goes back into the sickroom. The doctor exits, wiping his hands, with the servant, carrying the bowl of blood. Marianne lies, motionless and very pale. Elinor sits by her.

ELINOR. Marianne. Can you hear me? You cannot do this to me. I will not stand for it, you are being—very—ridiculous.

Beat.

I don't mean it. I'm sorry. I promise that if you get better, Marianne, I will never chide you again. Please, dearest—you cannot leave me. Do not leave me alone here. Please.

Lights fall on her holding Marianne's hand. Hours later. Elinor awakes, having fallen asleep next to Marianne. She feels her forehead, then starts. The doctor comes in and bends over Marianne. The sound of a carriage arriving. Elinor rushes out to meet her mother...

Willoughby's Visit

She hurries downstairs, only to see Willoughby. She immediately turns to go.

WILLOUGHBY. Miss Dashwood.

ELINOR. Your business cannot be with ME, sir. The servants must have forgotten to tell you that Mr. Palmer was not at home.

WILLOUGHBY. Had they told me that Mr. Palmer and all his relations were at the devil, it would not have turned me from the door!

Elinor turns to leave again.

How is your sister?

ELINOR. You have no right to ask.

He stands to block her way.

Mr. Willoughby!

WILLOUGHBY. Forgive me. I have been drinking.

83

ELINOR. What do you want?

WILLOUGHBY. …I want to make things right, if I can. I want something like forgiveness from Marianne.

ELINOR. "Marianne"?! You should not be so familiar.

WILLOUGHBY. Is she in as much danger as they say?

Elinor does not speak.

Is she dying?

Beat.

It is my fault, I know. Please let me see her.

ELINOR. No.

She turns to leave again.

WILLOUGHBY. I did not plan any of this! I never wanted to hurt anyone!

ELINOR. I must ask you to leave.

WILLOUGHBY. When I met your sister, I only wanted an idle dalliance. Something to do in the country.

ELINOR. Mr. Willoughby!

WILLOUGHBY. I mean—you misunderstand me—I thought that it was only a harmless flirtation! And at first, I thought that surely Marianne also knew that it could not lead to anything. You must see that it was impossible for me to seriously pursue a girl with no fortune, no station, no—forgive me—no notable family. But quite against my intentions, the part I played became the most pressing reality. I found myself most terribly in love.

ELINOR. —Did you?

WILLOUGHBY. I was going to ask her to marry me!

ELINOR. And what, precisely, stopped you?

He does not answer.

You must think me very foolish indeed.

WILLOUGHBY. My luck went bad. Mrs. Smith had somehow been informed of a…regrettable connection in my past.

ELINOR. I know your history, Mr. Willoughby.

WILLOUGHBY. I can guess who might have told you. Ask yourself if he is truly impartial! It was wrong, yes, I ought never to have touched Jane, but do not suppose that because I was a libertine, SHE was a saint!

ELINOR. Any weakness on her part is no excuse.

WILLOUGHBY. I assure you, Miss Dashwood, I have paid richly for my sins. Mrs. Smith pronounced me no gentleman, and I was summarily disinherited. I had many debts. Should I have gone to prison? I had no practical choice but to give up Marianne!

ELINOR. When you left Marianne that day, did you tell her that you would soon return?

WILLOUGHBY. I do not know what I told her, I was out of my head! I had to resolve to forget her entirely.

ELINOR. You did an excellent job—you ignored her letters, shunned her in public, exposed her to the worst kind of gossip and intrigue! Is this all evidence of the great love you have borne her?

WILLOUGHBY. Everything had already been settled between Miss Grey and me!

ELINOR. Then you have made your choice. And now you will be held to it. Goodbye.

WILLOUGHBY. I must see her.

> *He begins to push past her anyway.*

ELINOR. Seeing you will endanger her recovery!

WILLOUGHBY. Recovery!

ELINOR. Her fever broke last night. She is no longer in material danger.

WILLOUGHBY. Miss Dashwood. You have been very cruel.

ELINOR. As have you.

WILLOUGHBY. *(Sits heavily.)* You needn't punish me any more, Miss Dashwood. I am unhappy enough, I assure you. My marriage alone is just reward for my folly.

ELINOR. You should not speak of your wife in that way.

WILLOUGHBY. I shouldn't, should I? Yet— *"If ever on thine eyelid stood the tear / that pity had engendered, drop one here / this man was happy once, but conscience has her part / and writes a doomsday* sentence upon his heart." *(Upon Elinor's look of incomprehension.)* "Hope." The poem. Cowper.

ELINOR. You really should leave.

WILLOUGHBY. I will, before I make you hate me entirely. Miss Dashwood. Will you someday repeat to your sister what I have been telling you? Tell her that my heart was never unfaithful to her. Marianne is most probably lost to me forever. But were I, someday, by any blessed chance free again—

ELINOR. Mr. Willoughby.

WILLOUGHBY. Yes. Well. Goodbye, Miss Dashwood—God bless you!

ELINOR. Willoughby.

> *He stops.*

I do pity you.

Marianne Recovers

> *Willoughby exits. Mrs. Dashwood and Colonel Brandon arrive, very scared. Elinor meets them and Mrs. Dashwood almost collapses, embracing Elinor, pressing Colonel Brandon's hand. They support her into Marianne's room. She smooths back the hair from Marianne's head. Colonel Brandon watches from the doorway. The next day:*

MARIANNE. Colonel Brandon—

> *She holds out her hand.*

—I cannot thank you enough. You shall never know what it meant to me.

> *He takes her hand, gently. He bows, embarrassed, and turns to leave.*

MRS. DASHWOOD. If it is not an imposition, Colonel—would you stay? My voice is very weak and tired from the stress of yesterday's journey, but perhaps you could read to Marianne. We must make her confinement an interesting one.

> *Colonel Brandon turns back slowly, and sits by Marianne. He takes up a book—it's Shakespeare—and begins to read.*

86

> *He's surprisingly good. Marianne closes her eyes and turns towards him slightly. Elinor and her mother watch them.*

He loves her, of course.

ELINOR. To judge from his spirits, he does not think that there is much hope.

MRS. DASHWOOD. He thinks Marianne's affection and opinions too deeply rooted for any change, and even supposing her heart free again, does not believe that he could ever attach her.

MARIANNE. *(More gently than she spoke to Edward.)* Did you know, Colonel, that Shakespeare writes in a rhythm which matches precisely the beats of the human heart?... Ba-bum ba-bum ba-bum.

> *She opens her eyes and smiles at him. Colonel Brandon looks at her, then continues reading.*

MRS. DASHWOOD. Hm-hm!

The Recovery

Marianne and Elinor walk, slowly.

MARIANNE. And he had been drinking?

ELINOR. Yes—but I think he meant it all. Marianne...may I ask?

MARIANNE. Yes?

ELINOR. Do you perceive now that marriage to Willoughby would have condemned you to continual unhappiness? Can you imagine being bound forever to someone so endlessly selfish?

MARIANNE. Do you think him selfish?

ELINOR. The whole of his behavior from the beginning to the end of the affair, has been based on selfishness. His own pleasure, is, in every particular, his ruling principle.

MARIANNE. I suppose my happiness was never his object.

ELINOR. At present, he regrets marrying for money. And why does he regret it?—Because it has not made him perfectly happy. But had he married you, he would have always been poor, suffering all of poverty's attendant evils. He has already proven that he is capable of treating you with great cruelty and indifference when it suits his purposes; in those circumstances, who knows how you might have fared?

MARIANNE. Elinor...I agree with you. Are you surprised?

ELINOR. A little!

MARIANNE. I am glad we can speak about it. I am relieved to hear that he was not ALWAYS acting a part, not ALWAYS deceiving me; it makes me feel not quite such a fool. I think I may even understand how he justified his actions entirely.

ELINOR. Do you still acquit him?

MARIANNE. No. I assure you that I see everything as you desire me to. He was very wrong in what he did, and I never could have been happy with him after knowing how he treated that unfortunate girl. But I also feel sorry for him. Is that very foolish?

ELINOR. No. No, not at all.

MARIANNE. I am grateful that you told me, Elinor. I do not regret anything, I assure you—except my own behavior.

ELINOR. Do you compare your behavior with his?

MARIANNE. No. I compare it with what it ought to have been; I compare it with yours.

Long pause.

ELINOR. *(Moved.)* Well.

Pause, pokes her.

...You are a goose.

MARIANNE. We must turn back.

ELINOR. Are you tired?

MARIANNE. No. The Colonel has promised to read *The Tempest* with me this evening, and I don't wish to be late.

Elinor gives her a Look.

He's very good!

Edward Is Married

The Dashwoods sit in the dining room; Marianne picks at the piano. Thomas enters with a load of wood to tend the fire.

THOMAS. I suppose you know, ma'am, that Mr. Ferrars is married.

Marianne gives a violent start, fixes her eyes on Elinor, and falls back in her chair. Mrs. Dashwood does not know which child to turn to first.

Betsy! Miss Marianne is ill!

MARIANNE. No, no! I am fine.

MRS. DASHWOOD. Water, please. *(While he is pouring it:)* Who told you that Mr. Ferrars was married, Thomas?

THOMAS. I just saw his new bride, Miss Steele as was. She and Mr. Ferrars were stopping in a chaise outside the New London Inn. She said hello, and sent her best to the family—especially Miss Elinor—and I made free to wish her joy.

MRS. DASHWOOD. But she told you that she was married, Thomas?

THOMAS. Yes, ma'am. She smiled and said she was Mrs. Ferrars, now.

MRS. DASHWOOD. Was Mr. Ferrars with her?

THOMAS. I didn't see him, ma'am—but I imagine he is well enough, for she seemed vastly contented.

He leaves. Elinor sits very still.

MARIANNE. Elinor...

MRS. DASHWOOD. Margaret, go and...pick us some pretty flowers, won't you?

MARGARET. Oh. Yes.

She gets up and looks out the window on her way out.

Mamma, Colonel Brandon is at the gate.

MRS. DASHWOOD. For tea! Perhaps go and meet him, dearest. We—

MARGARET. —Mamma! It's not the colonel, it's Edward!

MRS. DASHWOOD. What?

MARGARET. It's Edward!

MARIANNE. Good God, it IS Edward!

ELINOR. I WILL be calm; I WILL be mistress of myself.

Marianne and Mrs. Dashwood fly to the other chairs and sit, Mrs. Dashwood attacking needlework, Marianne hiding her face as much as possible in a book.

MARIANNE. Sit, sit!

She pulls Margaret down roughly. Margaret sits. Elinor is frozen. Edward enters. He looks even more awkward than usual, and quite miserable and petrified.

MRS. DASHWOOD. Edward! *(Giving him her hand.)* I do wish you joy.

EDWARD. *(Very nervously.)* Ma'am.

Elinor has risen partway up and extended her hand, but sits quickly down again. She tries to smile. Marianne tries to look anywhere but at Edward. Margaret, thinking it incumbent on her to be dignified, takes a seat as far from him as she can, and maintains a strict silence, looking at the ceiling. A VERY AWFUL PAUSE.

MRS. DASHWOOD. I hope that you have left Mrs. Ferrars very well.

EDWARD. Rather well, I think. Yes.

Another pause. Elinor, resolving to exert herself, though fearing the sound of her own voice:

ELINOR. Is Mrs. Ferrars at Longstaple?

EDWARD. No, my mother is in town.

ELINOR. I meant *(Taking up some work from the table.)* to inquire after Mrs. EDWARD Ferrars.

She does not look up—but her mother and Marianne both swivel and stare at Edward.

EDWARD. Perhaps—perhaps you mean—Mrs. ROBERT Ferrars.

MARIANNE. Mrs. ROBERT Ferrars?!

MRS. DASHWOOD. Mrs. ROBERT Ferrars?!!

EDWARD. Perhaps you do not know—you may not have heard that my brother is lately married to—to Miss Lucy Steele.

MARIANNE. Your BROTHER?

Elinor sits with her head leaning so far over her work that it is practically in her lap.

EDWARD. …Yes. I had a letter from Miss Steele—now…Mrs. Robert Ferrars. She…they struck up an acquaintance. My brother is very popular, now, you see, because of his inheritance, and she, uh, set her cap at him, as I believe they say, and they were married last week.

Elinor BURSTS INTO NOISY TEARS and flees from the room. Her noisy sobs continue from behind the door, which she hurriedly slams behind her. Marianne, Margaret, and Mrs. Dashwood stand stiffly and rush out. Edward stands alone for a moment, looking foolish. Elinor is pushed back in by Marianne, who glares at both of them and slams the doors, locking them in.

Miss Dashwood…you must allow me to tell you how ardently…I am sensible of the impropriety…from the moment I first saw you… *(Sinking to his knee.)* Oh, Elinor. If I loved you any less, I might be able to talk about it more.

Elinor very insensibly almost kisses him. He is about to embrace her when:

ELINOR. Mr. Ferrars! *(Almost recovering her decorum—and momentarily pushing away.)* Mr. Ferrars, your behavior in this has been very wrong!

EDWARD. Very wrong! Very blameable! Elinor, when I met Lucy Steele, I was a very foolish, idle, ignorant, young man—I was not allowed to choose a profession and I had nothing to do but fancy myself in love—

ELINOR. But your behavior to me!

EDWARD. I was simple enough to think, that, because my FAITH was promised to another, there could be no danger in my being with you, and then when I *knew* I was in love, I thought, "The danger is only my own; I am doing no injury to anybody but myself!"

ELINOR. Mr. Ferrars!

EDWARD. But won't you forgive me, darling? Dearest Elinor, please. Won't you be mine?

ELINOR. …Edward.

> *She, finally, sinks down and meets him on his knees. They kiss. There is a soft knock on the door.*

MARGARET. Elinor? Mayn't we come in?

MARIANNE. Margaret!

MARGARET. Owww!

> *They throw open the doors. There is much hugging. Colonel Brandon walks up, for tea. Pointedly, Marianne leaves the circle and shyly gives him her hand, bringing him in. He shakes Edward's hand.*

MARIANNE. Elinor…

ELINOR. I know! I know!

> *The sisters embrace. Music starts. There is a dance which serves as the curtain call and wedding. Marianne and Elinor fasten veils and take Colonel Brandon and Edward's hands, respectively. We see them joined in marriage as the entire cast bows, and all is well.*

End of Play

APPENDIX

The following is optional additional text, created for overlapping dialogue at dinner scenes.

WILLOUGHBY. Miss Sophia is to call at Allenham tomorrow—she is a disputable beauty, don't you think? Lady Elizabeth called lately with Annamaria—they called, but I do not have anything more to say about them. They came and they sat and they went and made no impression whatsoever. And then the Sherers are to come next week—Mr. Sherer acts like an unsteady man. Dr. Mant gives him a very good character; what is wrong about him is to be imputed to his very terrible lady. I dare say the house may not thrive under its female government! I find her scarcely less frightening than her squash-faced pug lapdog, I don't mind telling you. At least the pug might be bribed with a little meat—I don't think Mrs. Mant will be swayed so easily. Perhaps I shall pitch bits of kidney at her next time I see her, and see if her temper is any improved.

MRS. JENNINGS. Dr. Parry recommended wintering at Bath to Lady B., of course. I suppose he will not mind having her close by, and helping himself to a few more of her ladyship's guineas! His system is a lowering one. He took twelve full ounces of blood from her when the gout appeared, and forbids wine. Can you imagine? I would drown myself at once, in the very water I was relegated to. With this austere treatment, he keeps on approving her pulse— keeps saying that it seems better than ever—but still will not let her be well! It is most provoking to her, I am sure, and still more provoking to her heirs, who presumably wish her to decide one way about her health or the other. Oh, now—you know I cannot help being naughty! I am the naughtiest woman alive, I assure you! I was a terror in my day, though I am toothless now!

COL. BRANDON. We had a delightful morning for our drive there. Very lovely. I enjoyed it thoroughly, but then the day turned off before we were ready, and we came home in some rain and the apprehension of a great deal. I do not seem to have taken a chill, though. There is nothing so difficult to shudder off as a nasty chill, be you ever so diligent with broths and teas and all manner of liquid comforts. Even the bone broths will not hold off a chill with any certainty. If I meet an unpleasant sort of individual in the street, with a particular expression—you know the sort—I often say to myself, I suppose they took a chill! And I daresay nine times out of ten I am correct.

LADY MIDDLETON [or for a woman, generally]. I saw some gauzes in a shop at Bath Street yesterday at only fourpence a yard, but they were not so good or so pretty as mine. I noticed that flowers are very much worn, of course, and fruit is still more the thing. Cassandra bought a bunch of strawberries for her little chapeau, and I have seen grapes, cherries, plums, and apricots. There are likewise almonds and raisins, French plums, and tamarinds—but at the grocers'. I have never seen any of them in hats. Not yet, that is! At this rate, we soon shall be balancing whole feasts on our heads, bread and meat and stews and all!

MARGARET. And do you know that a pony is less than fourteen hands, and a horse is more than fourteen hands? But not one of my hands, because my hands are too small to measure. Perhaps your hands are big enough, though, do you know? The grooms' were. You're not allowed, anyhow, anyhow, you're not allowed to put your hands on a horse without permission—from the horse that is. And how you get permission from a horse is that you come at it from the front very carefully and do not make any loud noises and that you are speak very low and kind to it. And you must not sneak up behind a horse—a horse or a pony—and make a loud noise, for it may kick you very hard because it is so very frightened. And that would be very grave indeed.

SIR JOHN. Pointers! I'll tell you of a pointer, now. You never saw such a fine bitch in the world as Mr. Palmer has—Mrs. Jennings' Charlotte's Mr. Palmer, that is. Oh, she has the keenest little nose, and such a howl—that's the pointer, I mean, not Charlotte, although if you ask Mr. Palmer! When he takes her out in the field—the pointer, again, the pointer—she flushes out anything that breathes. Once, once—she was chasing, you know, off like a flash, after some bird, we all were sure it was away, missed the shot, and I swear that she climbed a tree! Not a little—not a little tree, not a stump, no, any half-formed speck of a dog could climb a stump—I swear that this tree was a veritable…it seemed to span the sky!

MARIANNE. And do you know, they once locked him away, Cowper? In an insane asylum. People so often condemn that which they cannot understand. I think perhaps—perhaps—that imagination that propels him to such great heights, to such felicity can also drag him down into terrible depths. Thank the heavens that he found a way in which to channel his despair, even, into beauty! I love so dearly "Light Shining Out of Darkness"—do you know it? "God moves in a mysterious way / His wonders to perform; / He plants His footsteps in the sea / And rides upon the storm." It was his last hymn—he never wrote another after, for he felt that he was beyond redemption. It breaks my heart to think that someone who gave joy to so many, could not see his own value, the hope he gave to us all!

ELINOR. As I said to Marianne, "Norland probably looks much as it always does at this time of year. The woods and walks thickly covered with dead leaves—and not everyone has your passion for dead leaves." I do of course miss Norland—who would not—but the downs are unusually beautiful here. Although I do, of a walk, occasionally see the poor farmers and their families and think—I wish—that they might have better lodgings. I think that if there were a real scheme to improve their housing, we might see better yields and do our moral duty, simultaneously. Surely it is better to spend money in finding out how men can make the most of the land which supports them all, than in keeping dogs and horses only to gallop over it! I do not claim to know the answer to poverty in the countryside—but there is a reasonable solution, and it need not beggar our sportsmen.

MRS. DASHWOOD. And of course, they have turned out well—or are turning out well, I daresay, as Margaret is not quite fully formed—but when they were children! They used to run governesses distracted. Elinor was always very sweet, very obedient, but Marianne—she was sweet, also, I don't mean to mislead you, but she was very difficult to keep track of. You would turn your back, and she was gone, and half the time you would find her rolling about with the dogs in the mud, to the ruin of her little dress! One day, I came into the nursery—it was quite early, and I found Elinor, who was perhaps six or seven, reading quite calmly. I asked her, fearfully, where her sister was—it was far too quiet—and Elinor very sedately replied: "Do not fear, Mamma, she is in the other room. I have tied her to a desk so that she will not wander." Oh, I turned on my heel and ran out of the nursery and shut the door behind me instantly—so that she would not see me laughing! I was hard-pressed, I tell you.

EDWARD. I have no talent for description of the picturesque, and may offend you by my ignorance if we come to particulars. I will call hills "steep" which ought to be called "bold," surfaces "uneven" which ought to be called "rugged," and distant indistinct objects... uh, "distant," which ought to be described as "shimmering mysteriously through a haze." I am not much of a poet, I suppose. But I do find this very fine country—this comfortable and snug valley, with rich meadows and several neat farmhouses scattered here and there—and I daresay it must be a picturesque one, too, since you assure me it is so.

NOTE

In "Meet the Steeles," if you don't wish to set up the cottage interior again, the entirety of this scene (up until "Visit with the Steeles") may take place outside the cottage. In that case, strike this portion of Sir John's line: "Well, lay that work aside for one moment, Lady Industry;" and replace with: "Well, peep over this way for a moment, Miss Dashwood:"

PROPERTY LIST

(Use this space to create props lists for your production)

SOUND EFFECTS
(Use this space to create sound effects lists for your production)

Note on Songs/Recordings, Images, or Other Production Design Elements

Be advised that Dramatists Play Service, Inc., neither holds the rights to nor grants permission to use any songs, recordings, images, or other design elements mentioned in the play. It is the responsibility of the producing theater/organization to obtain permission of the copyright owner(s) for any such use. Additional royalty fees may apply for the right to use copyrighted materials.

For any songs/recordings, images, or other design elements mentioned in the play, works in the public domain may be substituted. It is the producing theater/organization's responsibility to ensure the substituted work is indeed in the public domain. Dramatists Play Service, Inc., cannot advise as to whether or not a song/arrangement/recording, image, or other design element is in the public domain.